DATE DUE

DEC 1 0 2003		

Demco, Inc. 38-293

THE MILKY WAY
galaxy number one

EXPLORING OUR UNIVERSE

THE MILKY WAY
GALAXY NUMBER ONE

BY FRANKLYN M. BRANLEY

ILLUSTRATED BY HELMUT K. WIMMER

THOMAS Y. CROWELL COMPANY

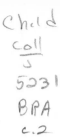
BY THE AUTHOR:

Experiments in the Principles of Space Travel
Solar Energy
Exploring by Satellite: The Story of Project Vanguard
Experiments in Sky Watching

Exploring Our Universe

The Nine Planets
The Moon: Earth's Natural Satellite
Mars: Planet Number Four
The Sun: Star Number One
The Earth: Planet Number Three
The Milky Way: Galaxy Number One

Manufactured in the United States of America
L.C. Card 68-27321
1   2   3   4   5   6   7   8   9   10

For Peg

ACKNOWLEDGMENTS

I wish to thank Dr. Vera C. Rubin of the Department of Terrestrial Magnetism, Carnegie Institution of Washington, for reading the book in manuscript and making many valued suggestions. I am also grateful to Karl Rubin for his help.

The photographs on pages 60, 62, 64, 65, 67, 88, 91, and 92 are reproduced by permission of the Mount Wilson and Palomar Observatories.

The illustration on pages 76-77, copyright 1958 by Lund Observatory, Sweden, is reproduced by permission of the observatory.

CONTENTS

1

EXPANDING BOUNDARIES

Look up at the stars tonight. Some are bright, others are dim. As the night goes by the panorama changes, for the stars rise and set. But this rising and setting is an illusion. Indeed, your view of the sky is deceptive and reveals very little of the truth. When observing conditions are favorable, anyone can see the broad cloudlike belt that extends from horizon to horizon. The ancients called this belt the Milky Way because of its appearance. The Greeks called it *galaxias kyklos*, or the "milky circle." The name has been assigned to the entire galaxy in which we are located. When we use the name Milky Way, we may be referring to either the broad belt across the sky, or to our entire galaxy. Your view gives you no feeling for the distances to the stars, no idea at all of the vast numbers of stars that there are, and certainly no conception of the shape and size of the Milky Way, the galaxy in which we are located.

Most of the information about our galaxy is less than one hundred years old, and much of it was discovered only within the last few decades. In this book we'll explore dilemmas that man has wrestled with in his attempts through the centuries to understand the nature of the sky above his head.

It may help to appreciate the struggle if you forget for a moment modern explanations for the motions of the sun, moon, planets, and stars that you observe, and for variations in the times and places of their rising and setting. Try to look at the sky through the eyes of people ignorant of the causes of such motions.

> Notice that the stars move, as described by an astute observer, from rising to setting in parallel circles, beginning to move upward from below as if out of the earth itself, rising little by little to the top, and then coming around again and going down in the same way until at last they disappear as if falling into the earth. After remaining some time invisible [you see the stars again] rising and setting as if from another beginning, and the times and also the places of rising and setting generally correspond in an ordered and regular way.

The paragraph above reads like a modern explanation of what one sees, but it was written more than eighteen hundred years ago by Claudius Ptolemy (A.D. 127–?151) of Alexandria, a Greek mathematician and astronomer who believed that the earth was motionless and that it was the center of the universe.

Ptolemy based his statement upon calculations made some three hundred years earlier by Hipparchus of Alexandria. He maintained that the sun, moon, and planets swept around the earth in circular paths, and the planets in turn moved in smaller circles that were centered on the larger ones. The observations of Hipparchus and Ptolemy are as true today as they were at the time of the writing. One who is ignorant of the makeup of the

Claudius Ptolemy (A.D. 127-151), Greek mathematician-astronomer who believed that the earth was the center of the "universe."

H. K. WIMMER

universe finds that his observations of the movements of the sun, moon, planets, and stars can be explained in another way: by saying the earth is standing still and all the objects in the sky are fastened to great spheres that turn around the stationary earth.

Although he probably died while still a young man, Ptolemy was able to explain during his short lifetime observations that learned men much older than he had pondered. He defined the structure of the solar system and the sky in the *Almagest*, a book that was to affect people's thoughts for generations. The Arabs gave the name *Almagest*, the "Greatest," to the book, for to them it was the greatest of all books. They regarded the work with awe and respect. Indeed, the *Almagest* was so considered by the civilized world for fourteen hundred years, a reign far longer than any other similar work has ever enjoyed.

Since Ptolemy, who was an authority, said that the earth stood still, it must be so. He said the earth was the center of the universe, and few people would deny such a great intellect. Also, his teachings agreed with what they could see.

However, there were some skeptics who questioned the ideas of Ptolemy. Beginning long before the first century there were individuals who believed the earth was moving through space in an orbit around the sun; the sun was the "master of the sky." Aristarchus of Samos (220?–143 B.C.) maintained that the earth spun around and that, as it spun, the earth moved through space. Such a belief was not at all popular, and Aristarchus suffered because of his statements.

Scores of generations of people lived during the centuries when Ptolemy's beliefs were accepted throughout the civilized world. Among these great numbers there must have been many philosophers who found it hard to accept that the universe was centered upon the earth. They might have thought the sun was the focal object, but they would not have dared express their thoughts. To do so would have invited the ridicule of one's friends and associates, for the idea was hard to understand. Even worse, such beliefs were contrary to church teachings that had been defined in the writings of St. Thomas Aquinas. Such people, if called upon to make explanations, would have been in awkward positions, indeed, for they had no proof of their beliefs. In fact, all observations indicated that the opposite was true—that the sky moved and the earth stood still.

If the astronomers who lived in the first thousand years of this era had been able to make accurate measurements, possibly the earth-centered conception would not have lasted so long. Angles could be measured only roughly, and the timing of observations could not be precise; the best timepieces of the day measured time only approximately. Until accurate timekeepers were available, one could not determine the exact moments of sunrise and sunset, or the times of the rising and setting of the planets.

Another reason why incorrect ideas persisted was that mathematical computations could not be made readily and efficiently. Just for numbering alone the only way available was the awkward procedure of the Romans. Multiplying the Roman numeral MMCCXXVII by DCCLXI is a major computation. To represent a small measurement, such as the distance to the moon, which averages about 238,857 miles, one would have to write in conventional Roman numerals CCXXXMMMMMMMMDCCC-LVII, or, using the super-bar (which multiplies a numeral by 1,000) for large numbers, $\overline{\text{CCXXXMMX}}$DCCCLVII. Imagine tables of data like these, and imagine using them in making complicated computations.

The Arabic system of notation, so called because it was popularly believed to have originated in Arabia, but which actually originated in India sometime about A.D. 500, provided a convenient and practical solution. But six hundred years were to pass before the system reached the academic centers of Europe. With the emergence of accurate clocks and the Arabic system of numbers, the movements of the planets could be timed to the second and their locations in the sky could be noted in a manageable fashion. Astronomers such as Ptolemy, and Hipparchus before him, had made the best observations and records possible with the equipment that was available to them. Now that observations could be made with greater accuracy, flaws and weaknesses were becoming apparent in the Ptolemaic idea, for the appearances of planets as timed by accurate devices and their movements across the sky did not agree with predictions.

Copernicus and the Period of Unrest

Twelve hundred years after Ptolemy's *Almagest*, the great mass of people were still oppressed by ignorance, just as they had been down through the centuries. Nicolaus Copernicus (1473–1543), a great Polish astronomer-mathematician, was one of the first scientists to break free of this oppression. When he was about twenty-five years old, Copernicus was convinced that Ptolemy's ideas were not correct, and that the sun not the earth was the center of the universe. It took him ten years to write a detailed account of his ideas. His great book was not published until late in his life. Indeed, the first copy was delivered to him on his deathbed in 1543. It was called *De Revolutionibus Orbium Coelestium*, or *On the Revolutions of the Celestial Spheres*.

Copernicus wrote:

Since there is no reason why the Earth should not possess the power of motion, we must consider whether in fact it has more motions than one, so as to be reckoned as a Planet.

That the Earth is not the center of all revolutions is proved by the apparently irregular motions of the planets and the variations in their distances from the Earth. These would be unintelligible if they moved in circles concentric with Earth. Since, therefore, there are more centers than one, we may discuss whether the center of the Universe is or is not the Earth's center of gravity.

Copernicus worked out a method of measuring the relative distances of the planets then known—Mercury, Venus, Earth, Mars,

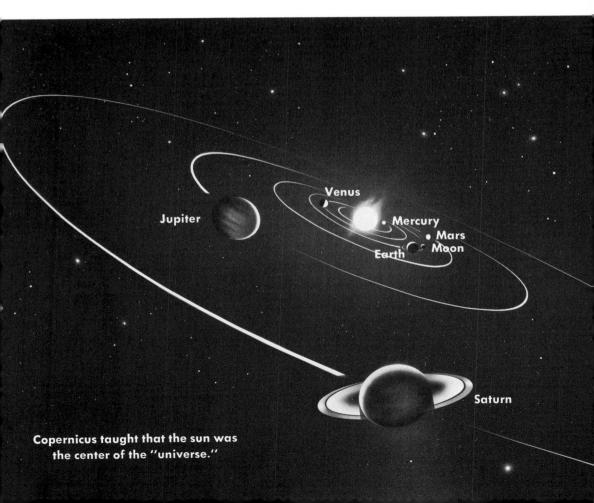

Copernicus taught that the sun was the center of the "universe."

Jupiter, and Saturn—and of placing them in correct relative locations. He developed his ideas thoroughly, and wrote in one passage:

> We therefore assert that the center of the Earth, carrying the Moon's path, passes in a great orbit among the other planets in an annual revolution around the Sun; that near the Sun is the center of the Universe; and that whereas the Sun is at rest, any apparent motion of the Sun can be better explained by the motions of the Earth.

Copernicus could not prove his beliefs. Because no proof was available, and because his ideas were revolutionary, the mass of people did not understand them, although the Church accepted them. Even the famous Danish astronomer Tycho Brahe (1546–1601) did not support Copernicus. Tycho designed and built in-

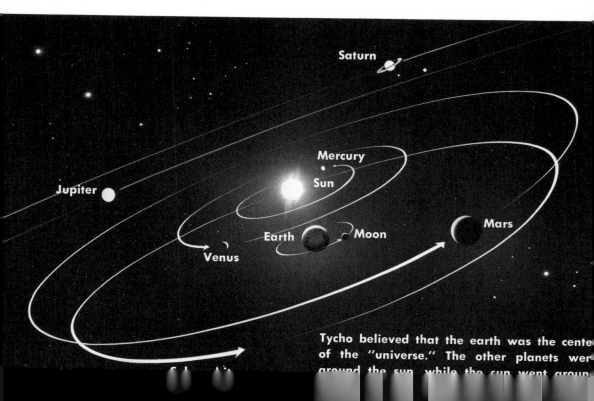

Tycho believed that the earth was the center of the "universe." The other planets were around the sun while the sun went around

struments that enabled him to make more accurate measurements of planetary positions than had ever been made up to that time. He was acclaimed throughout the world of the sixteenth century as the great astronomer of the period. In spite of his enlightenment in other respects, Tycho believed Copernicus was wrong. Tycho said that the sun went around the earth in a great circle, and Mercury, Venus, Mars, Jupiter, and Saturn went around the sun. This is the way he expressed his ideas in 1582, forty years after the death of Copernicus:

> I believe it is absolutely and undoubtedly necessary to have the Earth fixed at the center of the universe, following the opinion of the ancients and the testimony of the Scriptures. I do not agree at all with Ptolemy in assuming that the Earth is at the center of the orbits of the second mobile sphere; but I believe the celestial motions to be so arranged that only the Moon and the Sun, together with the eighth sphere, which is the remotest of all and encloses the others, have the center of their motion in the Earth. The five other planets revolve around the Sun, which acts as their king and master, and the Sun will always be at the center of their orbits, being accompanied by them in its annual motion. . . . Thus the Sun is the regulator and terminus of all these revolutions, and, like Apollo surrounded by the Muses, he governs the harmony of the heavens.

In 1616—some seventy-five years after the death of Copernicus—the Church declared that his book was "false and altogether opposed to the Holy Scripture."

A decade before this decree was made there were rumblings of things to come. Indeed, Giordano Bruno, an Italian astronomer, was burned at the stake in 1600 for trying to get people to accept the Copernican viewpoint. It was a time when one could not express such thoughts on pain of death. But he could think as he wished. And a famous thinker of those times of struggle was another Italian, Galileo Galilei, or more simply, Galileo (1564–1642), who was to become one of the outstanding astronomers of all time.

Galileo Provides Observational Information

Not only was Galileo a thinker, but he was a painstaking observer, experimenter, and teacher. He was destined to convince the world that Copernicus' idea of the nature of the universe was the correct one. He was able to establish that Ptolemy's earth-centered universe did not agree with the facts, or with the precise and accurate observations that were becoming possible.

In the sixty-seven years that followed the death of Copernicus, Tycho had lived and died, Bruno had been burned at the stake for teachings opposed to Church doctrine, and untold numbers of courageous scholars had been ridiculed and condemned for daring to support the sun-centered conception of the universe. Try as they might, the champions of Copernicus could offer no proof at all that they were right. Their beliefs were considered to be little more than conjecture, for no convincing arguments were offered in support of the viewpoint.

When well-informed people have held a belief for scores of generations, their ideas cannot be changed by mere argument. In the 1600's the mass of people were uneducated and believed only in those things they could experience firsthand. Something that they could understand was needed to change their ideas of the universe, something that people in the street could see. Galileo provided that essential ingredient.

Using a telescope to scan the skies—the first man to do so—

Galileo Galilei (1564-1642), Italian astronomer—first to see the rings of Saturn, the satellites of Jupiter, and the phases of Venus.

Galileo discovered that Venus goes through a complete cycle of changes, just as the moon does. And the size of the planet appears to change a great deal, indicating that it moves successively away from the earth and toward the earth. The only way to explain the changes in the size and phase of Venus was to assume the planet was in orbit around the sun, and between the sun and the earth. When Venus is viewed with the unaided eye, it is sometimes quite dim, while at other times it is the brightest object in the sky, exceeded only by the sun and moon. But the planet always appears disklike. When viewing Venus telescopically, the observer sees the planet as a crescent, a full disk, a gibbous planet; he sees a complete phase cycle. Here was something people could see simply by looking through a "magic tube," as the telescope was often called, and it was convincing.

But Galileo made another, equally important, discovery. He discovered Io, Europa, Ganymede, and Callisto, the four major satellites of Jupiter. Since his time eight more have been discovered, the last in 1951. Galileo watched the satellites night after night, and he could see them changing position from one side of Jupiter to the other as they moved in orbits around the planet. Here was proof of the Copernican theory. All objects did not go around the earth, for here were objects going around Jupiter.

Thereafter, knowledge of the motions of the planets and satellites grew rapidly. More and more it appeared that the universe was sun-centered, as Copernicus had said it was.

The Universe of Sun, Moon, Planets

Learned men who lived in the seventeenth and eighteenth centuries believed that the entire universe was the sun and moon and the planets—all encased within a great sphere of stars. In essence, it had been the belief of multitudes of generations that had observed the sky down through the ages. The universe of sun, moon, and planets was observed against a fixed background of stars. And that was essentially the sum total of man's comprehension of the stars. The stars were unimportant and inconsequential backgrounds for the more important parts of the universe: sun, moon, and planets, which people believed affected their lives deeply, and which certainly changed position continually from night to night, week to week, and year to year.

A few details of the stars themselves had been observed, but only infrequently. For example, slight changes in the positions of a limited number of stars had been noted by astute sky watchers. Other observers noted that some stars were brighter than others. Such observations did not receive much attention, for they were not usually spectacular, and stars were not nearly as important as planets. In 1604 Johannes Kepler (1571–1630), who had achieved renown in scientific circles, had reported a star that increased a hundred-thousandfold in brightness. The star became so bright that it could be seen during the brightest parts of the day. And before that Tycho Brahe had reported a similar observation of a different star. These two stars were classified as *novas*, from the Latin word for "new," because the stars appeared to be new ones —becoming highly visible for brief periods and suddenly decreasing in brilliance so much that they could be seen no more. However, they are not really new stars, but very faint stars which have brightened dramatically. Such observations of stars were spectacular, but they were rare, and did not excite people nearly as much as did planets—or comets, which were thought to be omens of evil, signs from the gods of calamity, famine, pestilence, and disease.

Other peculiarities of stars had been seen on a few occasions. In 1596 an astronomer noticed a star in the constellation of Cetus, the Whale, that brightened suddenly, then disappeared. He thought it was a nova, another one of those so-called new stars, and similar to the star seen by Tycho. But some forty years later the same star was observed by a second astronomer. So it could not have been a nova, for they did not recur—they flared up, died down, and disappeared. He kept careful watch of the star over a period of several years and discovered that it changed in brightness in a regular period of eleven months. The star is now called Mira Ceti, the "miraculous one in the Whale." It was the first variable star, or star that varies in brightness in a regular pattern, to be identified.

In the seventeenth and eighteenth centuries other astronomers made painstaking sightings of many stars, and found that there were several that varied in brightness. Some took only a few days to complete a cycle from bright to dim to bright; others took much longer.

Seventeenth-century sky watchers who used telescopes noted other features of the stars. For example, they observed that Mizar, the star at the bend of the handle of the Big Dipper, was in reality two stars. Rapidly thereafter, careful observations revealed there were numerous instances where two stars existed, although the casual observer could see only one.

Centuries of sky watching had revealed little more about the stars. However, man's early knowledge of the sky that formed a background for the planets did not stop with the stars, for hazy patches of lighted material had been seen here and there. They were called *nebulae* (or nebulas, as we often call them today) after a Latin word for "mist" or "vapor," because of their filmy, nebulous appearance. In the early 1600's the Great Nebula in Andromeda had been noted; also the impressive bright nebula just below the belt stars of Orion.

After the telescope was introduced to astronomers, a favorite occupation was to scan the sky for comets. The discovery of a comet invariably brought fame, and often fortune, to the discoverer, largely because comets were suspected of having strong and mystical effects on people who actually observed them. Many times nebulas were mistakenly identified as comets. To avoid such errors, the French astronomer Charles Messier (1730–1817), who was a comet hunter himself, catalogued 103 hazy, nebulous objects in 1771. This prevented astronomers from making reports of comets they thought they had discovered but which, on further investigation, proved to be a quite different kind of formation and one that did not have any fame associated with it.

Knowledge of the space and objects beyond the universe as it was believed to be at that time (the sun, moon, and planets) was limited, and often incorrect. Men did not know what the stars were, nor did they know where the stars were, for stellar distances had not been determined. Many observers developed models of the way stars were arranged. Invariably they distributed them upon spheres, and all stars were the same distance from a central point.

Herschel and a New Look at the Universe

An entirely new perspective on the universe was presented to the world at the end of the eighteenth century and the beginning of the nineteenth when William Herschel appeared on the scene.

Herschel, a musician who was born in Hanover, Germany, in 1738, left that country for England when he was nineteen years old. He was an accomplished organist, teacher, and composer who also was keenly interested in science and philosophy. His interest in astronomy was somewhat hampered because the telescopes available to him were inferior. They produced dim, distorted images that were unsatisfactory. So Herschel decided to make his own telescope. His first efforts were so successful that he made scores of instruments. Some of these he used himself, but the larger number were sold. Each success that Herschel achieved encouraged him to make an even better instrument. His most successful one, the telescope that he used to make the observations for which he is famous, was twenty feet long and had a metal mirror nineteen inches in diameter. Herschel built a much larger telescope, but did not use it very much. It was forty feet long and had a metal mirror fifty-eight inches in diameter. But the device was large and clumsy. A whole crew of men was needed to move it and adjust the lenses, and the images it produced were distorted, probably because the mirror sagged owing to its great weight.

Since the days of Ptolemy, and no doubt ages before, men had realized that some stars were brighter than others. But they had no idea why this was so. In almost every instance explanations were associated with size—the larger stars were the brighter ones. This was because all the stars were thought to be contained on the surface of a great sphere at the same distance from the earth.

Herschel surmised that all stars were the same. They were distributed evenly in space, and differences in brightness were caused by only one factor, differences in distance. Heretofore, those who thought about the stars had all manner of explanations for these differences. Some said that stars were really holes punched in a dark, all-encompassing sky. Brightness beyond could be seen through the holes. Some holes were larger and so brighter than others. Others had believed that stars were different-size objects affixed to a solid, black sky. In all cases the sky was thought to be two dimensional—entirely lacking in depth— and so Herschel's idea was revolutionary.

Using his fine 19-inch telescope, and applying careful, painstaking procedures, Herschel made extensive contributions to man's knowledge. He discovered the planet Uranus, and thus

William Herschel (1738-1822), German-English astronomer—builder of fine telescopes, discoverer of Uranus.

H.K. WIMMER

doubled the known size of the solar system. Before this, Saturn, at a distance from the sun of some 886 million miles, was thought to be at the outermost limit of the solar system. Uranus is 1,782 million miles from the sun, more than twice as far away. In addition Herschel made important studies of sunspots and the rings of Saturn. He also discovered two of the satellites of Uranus and two new satellites of Saturn. These investigations alone were enough to make Herschel a giant of astronomy. But it was the realm of the stars that provided the major challenge to Herschel. And his conclusions, courageous because they were contrary to most beliefs, were to change forever man's idea of the universe.

Night after night, year after year, Herschel painstakingly studied the stars. Repeated observations enabled him to record almost one thousand double stars—stars that appeared to be very close together. He continued to study certain of these stars, and by keeping very accurate records, was able to determine that the stars changed position with respect to one another. He established that these changes could be caused in no way other than by the motion of both stars around their common center of gravitation. Here was an observation that proved there were "world" systems other than the solar system, and other than the system of Jupiter and its satellites discovered by Galileo.

Men began to look with some doubt on their narrow notions of the nature and extent of the universe. What really was the universe? How large was it? What was it made of? All perplexing questions in the eighteenth century, as indeed they still are today.

The casual sky observer of antiquity or of modern times sees with the unaided eye that the stars are not evenly distributed. In some regions there seem to be great spaces between the stars. And, at the other extreme, there are regions where the stars are so

The Sagittarius region of the Milky Way is rich in stars. The view is toward the center of the galaxy. Altair, Deneb, Vega are the three bright stars in the upper half of the painting.

close together that they cannot be separated one from the other. There appear to be vast clouds of stars.

The nature of the "milky" clouds, as the Greeks named them, was not at all clear until 1610 when Galileo studied the formation with his telescope. What a revelation that first view must have been. In his book *The Starry Messenger* Galileo presented his conclusions:

> The next object which I have observed is the essence or substance of the Milky Way. By the aid of a telescope anyone may behold this in a manner which so distinctly appeals to the senses that all the disputes which have tormented philosophers through so many ages are exploded at once by the irrefragable evidence of our eyes, and we are freed from wordy disputes upon this subject, for the Galaxy [the Milky Way] is nothing else but a mass of innumerable stars planted together in clusters. Upon whatever part of it you direct the telescope straightway a vast crowd of stars presents itself to view; many of them are tolerably large and extremely bright, but the number of small ones is quite beyond determination . . . .

After Galileo had shown the world the tremendous value of the telescope for observing objects in the sky, other astronomers of the 1600's made their own telescopes. Or, as often was the case, Galileo supplied them with instruments he had made himself.

Scores of instruments were made by Galileo and others. Effectiveness increased rapidly from the crude and limited 32-power instrument that Galileo used to make his momentous discoveries. In the century following many men must have observed the Milky Way. Yet, as far as the literature reveals, no one had ventured

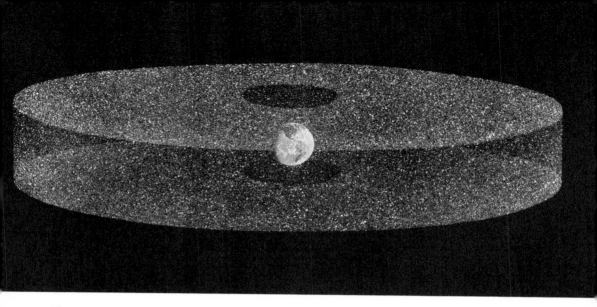

Thomas Wright believed that the galaxy was shaped like a grindstone. This was man's first attempt to give shape to our star system.

an explanation that had any more to it than Galileo's statement.

Almost 150 years later, in 1750, Thomas Wright (1711–1786) of Durham, England, wrote a book called *An Original Theory of the Universe*. The book contains the first attempt to describe the shape of our galaxy, and how it is that we see the Milky Way arching across the sky. Wright proposed that the galaxy is shaped like a grindstone, and that we are at the center. When we look up or down we see few stars because the galaxy (the grindstone) is thin at those places. When we look "around the grindstone," we see large numbers of stars, so many they appear as clouds.

This conception was very popular at the time and had many champions. But the theory itself and all changes and modifications were based on conjecture alone. No one had assembled the information needed to support the theory. It remained for William Herschel to make this giant step.

When he turned his telescope to the Milky Way, Herschel was able to see more clearly the separate stars mentioned by Galileo. He assumed that the stars were equally luminous, and that they were scattered evenly throughout space. Differences in brightness would therefore be due to differences in distance.

Herschel aimed his telescope at different points in the sky and counted the number of stars that he could see. If only a few stars were seen, he believed the stars could not extend very far into space. If the stars were numerous, they must extend much farther, for Herschel believed stars were distributed evenly. From the number of stars that could be seen, Herschel could gauge how far the stars extended in that direction. He called the procedure "Gaging [gauging] the Heavens."

Herschel made more than three thousand counts. He plotted the positions he judged the stars occupied. Out of this great work evolved the first attempt to picture the galaxy. Herschel had made star counts of all observable parts of the sky. Also, Herschel knew

Herschel "gauged the stars"; he counted them in each segment of the sky. Field of view is cone shaped.

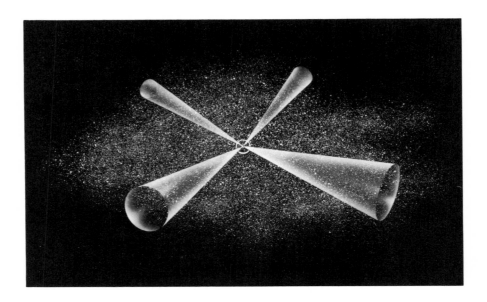

that the observer at the telescope examines stars in a long, narrow cone—and the observer is at the point (or vertex) of the cone. In certain directions the star counts were much greater than they were in other directions. If only a few stars were seen when looking in a given direction, the cone must be shorter than when a larger number were seen.

From this knowledge, Herschel was able to make a model of the shape of the whole formation of stars. All he had to do was to figure out the length of each cone. It was well known that when the length of a cone is doubled, the volume becomes eight times greater. Therefore, a part of the sky (a star gauge) that contains eight times as many stars as another star gauge must be twice as long. By such reasoning, Herschel arrived at the first model of the galaxy. The Milky Way (galaxy) was shown to be divided into two branches.

According to Herschel, the sun was at the center of the formation: a perfectly logical supposition, since at that time there was

Herschel's drawing of the Milky Way Galaxy, man's first attempt that was based on actual observations.

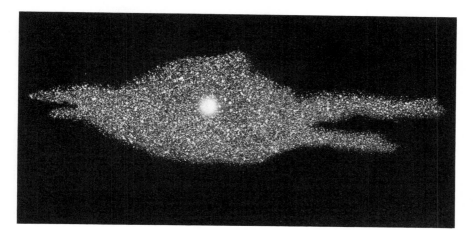

no reason to believe otherwise. One had to assume that stars were distributed evenly around the observer. Herschel had given new dimensions to the universe. Before his time men had believed that the solar system was the universe. Now the stars were considered an integral part of the whole. As Herschel wrote in one of his many scientific papers,

> That the Milky Way [galaxy] is a most extensive structure of stars of various sizes admits no longer of the least doubt; and that our sun is actually one of the heavenly bodies belonging to it is as evident. I have now viewed and gauged this shining zone in almost every direction and find it composed of stars whose number, by the account of these gauges, constantly increases and decreases in proportion to its apparent brightness to the naked eye.

Herschel's belief that stars were distributed evenly, and differed in brightness only because of variations in distance, was reasonable, even though at that time people had little conception of the distance to a star. No way had been found to measure the distance. And no way had been discovered of determining that some stars were much farther away from us than were others.

Until more reliable information concerning distances to the stars was available, astronomers could not explore their ideas of the manner in which the galaxy (or universe, as it was then thought to be) was put together. Less than twenty years after the death of William Herschel a way of finding distances to the stars was found.

2

MEASURING DISTANCES

IN THE early part of the nineteenth century Friedrich Wilhelm Bessel (1784–1846), a German astronomer and mathematician, equipped an observatory with the most modern and precise instruments that men had devised up to that time. With these instruments he could determine the position of a star with considerable accuracy. And he was able to perceive that certain stars appeared to shift slightly when observed at six-month intervals. This apparent shift of a star is called stellar parallax. It is a phenomenon that results not because the star actually moves, but because the star is observed from two positions in earth's orbit—positions separated by 186 million miles, the diameter of the orbit.

Parallax is an effect that you can observe by holding a pencil upright at arm's length from you. Look at the pencil with one eye only—close the other eye. Then alternately open and close one eye and then the other. The pencil will appear to shift from left to right and right to left. This is *parallax*, from a Greek word that means "a slight motion."

Time after time Bessel observed with great care the star 61 Cygni (star number 61 in the constellation Cygnus) and recorded its position. Six months later, when the earth was 186 million miles from its original position, he observed the star again. He checked that position against the original location and found that the star had shifted ever so slightly. The shift was only 0.3 of one second of arc. A circle, as you know, is divided into 360 degrees. Each degree is then divided into 60 minutes, each minute into 60 seconds. Therefore 0.3 of a second is three-tenths of one-sixtieth of one-sixtieth of 360 degrees. Such a slight amount of parallax could not have been determined at all without the most precise measuring devices. Yet that minuscule displacement was enough for Bessel to measure the distance to 61 Cygni. Once the distance to this star had been found, men had to change their ideas about the placement of the stars, and answers other than those that had been suggested had to be found to explain differences between stars that Herschel and others had observed.

Before proceeding further with our story, let's see how stellar parallax enables one to compute the distance to a star.

In geometry, all information about a triangle can be found when and if we know any three parts of the triangle in order. For example, if we know an angle, side, angle—or side, angle, side— we can construct the triangle. Suppose we wanted to find the distance to the moon. We can do it by constructing a triangle. Two observers on earth at a known distance apart, 5,000 miles for example, observe the same location on the moon. They measure the angle produced by the line connecting the two observers and the line of observation. All they need do to find the distance to the moon is to construct a triangle to scale: one inch to 10,000 miles, for example. The line connecting the observers would be ½ inch long, and they construct a triangle using the same angles that the observers measured when looking at the moon. When the

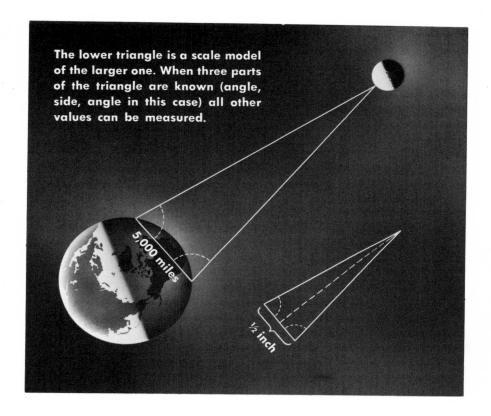

The lower triangle is a scale model of the larger one. When three parts of the triangle are known (angle, side, angle in this case) all other values can be measured.

5,000 miles

½ inch

altitude of the triangle is measured on the scale drawing, it will give to scale the distance to the moon at the time the measurements were made. In this example the line would be about 24 inches long, representing 240,000 miles.

This procedure of constructing a scale model of the triangle can be used when the distances are relatively short and the scale triangle is small and manageable. It cannot be used for stellar distances because the scale needed to represent such great distances is unreasonable. Other methods must be used to measure distance to the stars. Here's the way Friedrich Bessel did it, and the way it is done today:

We start out with a drawing (page 28) showing the earth's orbit around the sun. Then a star at A is seen at A' when the earth is at position 1. Six months later, when the earth is at 2, the star is seen at A″. The angle A′ → A″ on the sky is equal to twice the parallax of the star. But we can say the same thing a different way. If we draw a triangle Star → Sun → Earth, then the angle at the star is equal to the parallax of the star. For a star closer to the sun, at B, the angle is larger, so the parallax is greater. If the star at C is twice as close as the star at A, then its parallax is twice as large.

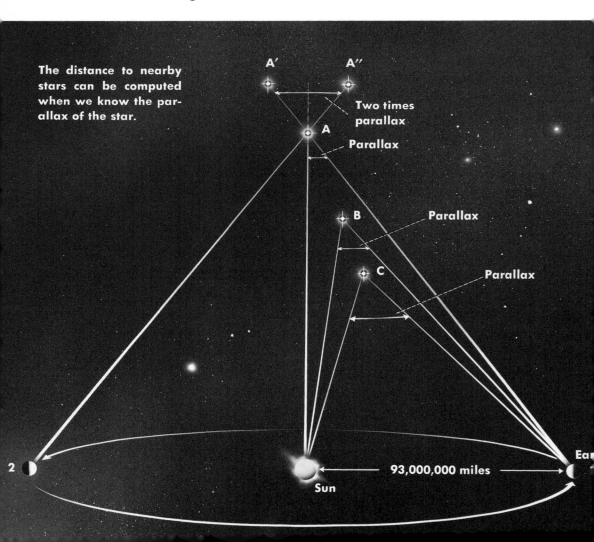

The distance to nearby stars can be computed when we know the parallax of the star.

From the geometry of the triangle, knowing the base is 93,-000,000 miles, we can calculate that for a star with a parallax angle equal to one second, the distance of the star is 19,200,000,-000,000 miles. This means that the star 61 Cygni, with a parallax of only 0.3 second is farther away. In fact, it is 1/0.3 times as far, or 63,942,000,000,000 miles away.

To get figures that are easier to manage, the astronomer uses the light-year as a unit for measurement. This is the distance that light travels in one year at a steady velocity of 186,000 miles a second. The number of miles in a light-year is found by multiplying 186,000 by the number of seconds in a year. We find that one light-year equals about 5.9 trillion miles.

Therefore, to find the distance in light-years to 61 Cygni, which we figured was 63,942,000,000,000 miles away, you divide the distance by 5.9 trillion miles, and it turns out to be 10.8 light-years from us. This figure was later corrected to 11.2 light-years, the figure that is currently accepted. Later in that same year Thomas Henderson, an English astronomer who was observing from South Africa, found that Alpha Centauri had the largest parallax of any star—0.76 second. This meant that the star was only 4.3 light-years away—making it the star nearest to the solar system. (You may have read that the star nearest the solar system is Proxima Centauri rather than Alpha Centauri, and wondered which is correct. The star Alpha Centauri is actually a system of three stars, one of which is Proxima Centauri. The three stars are in orbit around one another, such that at enormous intervals of time Proxima Centauri is 4.25 light-years from us.)

At the same time that Henderson was in South Africa, Friedrich Struve, a Russian astronomer, was working at the Pulkovo Observatory, which he established. He found that the bright star Vega, in the constellation of Lyra, was 27 light-years away.

Stellar Magnitudes

In the decades since 1838 the distances to scores of stars have been determined by observing their parallaxes. However, the method works only when the star is no farther than 400 light-years away. The maximum practical distance is more nearly 250 to 300 light-years. At 400 light-years the parallax angle is only 0.008 second. It is impossible to measure such a small angle accurately. Indeed, one second of parallax is the same as the angle subtended by a diameter of one inch from a distance of one and a half miles. Because of this severe limitation only a small fraction of stellar distances could be computed, for most stars are much farther away than 200 to 300 light-years. The parallaxes of only about seven thousand stars have been measured with an accuracy of 10 percent or better.

To determine the distances to stars beyond the limit possible by the parallax method other procedures have to be used.

If every star were actually as bright as every other star, as Herschel believed, the distance to each star could be quite easily determined. If we know two lights are the same brightness, yet one appears dimmer than the other, then we know that the dimmer light is farther away. And we can determine how much farther it is from us, because light varies inversely as the square of the distance. Therefore, a star that appears one-fourth as bright as another identical star would be twice as far away. One that is one-ninth as bright would be three times farther, and so on. This would be true only if the space between the stars were free of gas and dust which could scatter the starlight and make the stars appear dimmer. We will see later on that we do live in a dusty galaxy, so the problem of the distances of the stars is made even more complicated.

But today we know that stars are not equally bright. Stars vary in color, size, composition, temperature, and brightness. Some stars are not bright at all when compared to others. They appear bright only because they are nearby. The sun, for example, is certainly the brightest of all the stars as far as we are concerned, but only because it is so close to us. The distance to the sun, 93 million miles, is insignificant when compared with distances to other stars. The next nearest star beyond the sun appears as only a point of light. It is about 26 trillion miles from us. Actually it is about 15 percent more luminous than the sun.

When speaking of the brightness of a star as observed from the earth, we use the term magnitude. The system was devised by the Greek astronomer Hipparchus in the second century B.C. He could discern six variations or differences in the brightness of stars. He said that the brightest stars were first magnitude, and the dimmest were sixth magnitude. Whether a star was one magnitude or another was determined purely by judgment of the observer. And the observer had no telescope or other instruments to aid him. Today astronomers measure the light of a star carefully, and give definite mathematical values to the different magnitudes, or brightnesses. The variation from one step to the other is 2.5, thus a second-magnitude star is 2.5 times dimmer than one of the first magnitude, a third-magnitude star is 2.5 times dimmer than one of the second magnitude, and so on. Thus a sixth-magnitude star is $2.5 \times 2.5 \times 2.5 \times 2.5 \times 2.5$, or 100 times dimmer than one of first magnitude. If you multiply 2.5 times itself five times, the answer will be nearly 100—a first-magnitude star is 100 times brighter than a sixth-magnitude star. Or we could say it in another way: If the brightest star (first magnitude) is given a brightness value of 100, then the other magnitudes will have brightness equal to—40, 16, 6.3, 2.5, and 1.

The data of Hipparchus were incomplete, and they were based on opinion. Today we have more reliable facts because we have instruments to measure accurately the light that a star or the sun or a planet gives off and so know how bright it really is. We have found that stars may be brighter than first magnitude. Such magnitudes are preceded by a minus sign. Thus, Sirius, the brightest star in the night sky, is magnitude —1.43, the full moon is magnitude —12.6, and the sun's magnitude is —26.5. Some interesting facts concerning magnitudes are listed in the table here.

A TABLE OF MAGNITUDES

Object	Magnitude
Sun	—26.5
Full moon	—12.6
Venus (brightest)	—4.0
Jupiter (brightest)	—2.0
Mars (brightest)	—2.0
Sirius	—1.4
Aldebaran	1.0

Under ideal conditions—clear, black sky—a person can see objects down to the sixth magnitude; the limit with binoculars is tenth magnitude. The extreme magnitude that can be seen with a 6-inch telescope is 13. An observer at the 200-inch telescope can see down to the twentieth magnitude; and a camera attached to that telescope can pick up objects down to magnitude 23.5.

There are many ways of measuring the magnitude, or brightness, of a star. The most obvious way is to observe the star visually and so arrive at the visual, or apparent, magnitude. The brightness of the star might be compared with some standard star. Vega is often used for this purpose because it has a magnitude of 0.1—very close to magnitude 0. There are only three stars that match the brightness of Vega, or are brighter. They are

Alpha Centauri, Canopus, and Sirius. Alpha Centauri, which can be seen in the Southern Hemisphere, has a magnitude of 0.1— the same as that of Vega. Canopus has a magnitude of —0.9; Sirius, with a magnitude of —1.43, has the greatest magnitude of all stars, other than the sun.

Visual magnitudes are of necessity subjective, and so open to considerable question. The camera gives a much more objective evaluation. A photograph of the star is made and a measurement of the brightness of the image provides the photographic magnitude of the star.

Another way of measuring the brightness of a star is to focus the light onto a photoelectric cell—the amount of current varying directly with brightness. A fourth method is to focus the light onto a device that measures the radiant energy given off by the star. This provides radiometric magnitude.

Each of the procedures used for measuring brightness has both advantages and disadvantages. For example, the human eye is more sensitive to red light than are ordinary photographic emulsions. Therefore a star that produces a large amount of red light will appear brighter to the eye than it will appear on a photograph.

Ordinary film is not sensitive to infrared light, but these particular wavelengths do affect radiometric magnitude. Therefore, a star may not be especially bright according to visual and photographic measurements, but it may prove to be very bright when measured by radiometric techniques.

Brightness, or magnitude, of a star has meaning when it can be compared with another star. Then we can say that a given star is so many times brighter, or dimmer, than the other.

By observing a star with the unaided eye, a camera, or a radiometer, we can determine its apparent magnitude, how bright the star appears to be. Using this information we can figure out how bright the star really is. We can find the real brightness, or real magnitude, of the star. We call the real magnitude of a star its absolute magnitude.

If a star is within about three hundred light-years, we can determine the distance to the star by measuring its parallax. Once we know these two things, we can figure out mathematically, or simply by comparison, how bright the star would appear if it were at any other distance. For example, we know that the star would appear one-fourth as bright if the star were twice as far away; it would appear one-ninth as bright if the star were three times farther away. Also, we can compare one star with another to determine differences in their real brightness.

Suppose we wanted to know if one star is really brighter than another, or if it only appears brighter because it is nearer. We can figure out how bright the two stars would be if we were able to observe them at the same distance. Of course we cannot observe them at the same distance, but we can calculate how bright each star would be if placed at a distance of ten parsecs—or 32.6 light-years. (Parsec is made of the two words—*parallax* and *second*. A star having a parallax of one second would be 3.26 light-years away.) The brightness which a star would have at a distance of 10 parsecs is defined as the real, or absolute, magnitude of the star.

For example, we know that the apparent magnitude of the sun is —26.5. The distance of the earth from the sun is 93 million miles. Suppose we could place the sun at the standard distance of 10 parsecs—32.6 light-years. The sun would then be about 2 million times farther away than it actually is. We know that the amount of light received from any object varies inversely with the square of the distance; double the distance, the light is one-fourth as great; triple the distance, the light is one-ninth as great; and so on. Therefore, when the sun is at 10 parsecs, the light we receive would be $1/2,000,000^2$ as much, or $1/4,000,000,000,000,000$ of what we ordinarily receive. This difference amounts to nearly 31.5 magnitudes. This means that if the sun were 10 parsecs away from us, it would appear 31.5 magnitudes dimmer. Its magnitude is —26.5, therefore its absolute magnitude is —26.5 plus 31.5, or +5. The sun would be a star so dim that it would be very difficult to see, except under the best sky conditions. (See the appendix for an explanation of the mathematics involved in the process.)

In the same fashion we can find the absolute magnitudes of stars when their apparent magnitudes and distances are known. Suppose that a star appears to be a tenth-magnitude star, and it is 100 parsecs away. If the star were moved to a distance of only 10 parsecs, it would be ten times closer. Therefore, it would be one hundred times brighter, corresponding to a difference of 5 magnitudes. The real magnitude of the star would be 10 minus 5, or 5.

The sun seems to be billions of times brighter than Sirius, the brightest star in the night sky. But if Sirius and the sun were both 10 parsecs away, twenty-six suns would be needed to match the brightness of Sirius.

Cepheid Variables

To reach a fuller understanding of the arrangement of the stars in our galaxy, different methods of measuring distances were needed, for the procedure discussed above applies only to near-by stars.

In the early part of this century Miss Henrietta Leavitt, an astronomer at Harvard College Observatory, discovered a way of measuring extreme distances within our galaxy, and also of measuring distances to galaxies beyond our own. She found that the absolute magnitudes of certain variable stars could be inferred if you could see them well enough to determine their period of variation. There are many stars that do not shine with a steady light, but which vary in brightness. The reasons for these variations are not well understood. However, for our purposes we are only concerned with the fact that brightness does change.

Variable stars, you recall, were first observed by Kepler and Tycho Brahe. These variable stars can be seen in distant parts of our own galaxy.

Miss Leavitt studied many photographs of the Smaller Magellanic Cloud, a vast collection of stars outside our own galaxy, and all about the same distance away from us. She detected Cepheid variable stars (so-called because this type of star was first observed in the constellation Cepheus). She measured the average apparent brightness of the stars and their periods, the time required for them to go from bright to dim and back again.

After studying these data, Miss Leavitt discovered that the longer it took the star to go from dimmest to brightest and back to dimmest, the brighter the star appeared to be. This single discovery gave astronomers a yardstick that was valuable for measuring large astronomical distances. Let's see how it could be used for this purpose.

You remember that apparent magnitude depends upon two things: how far away the star is and how bright the star really is. All the stars that Miss Leavitt observed were at the same distance. Therefore, although the distance was unknown at the time, any differences in apparent brightness had to be due to differences in real brightness—for the distances of all the different variable stars were essentially the same.

However, before an absolute magnitude could be assigned to variable stars whose apparent magnitude Miss Leavitt had observed in the collection of stars beyond our own, it was necessary to measure the absolute magnitude of some Cepheid variable inside our galaxy. In order to do this, she had to know the distance.

In our whole galaxy there was not a single Cepheid variable star close enough so astronomers could measure its distance by finding its parallax. You recall that the parallax method cannot be used for stars farther away than three hundred light-years.

But astronomers, like other researchers, look for other, and perhaps not quite so obvious, solutions. They found another way of measuring the distances to faraway stars. If the motions of stars are studied carefully, their distances can be estimated, because the farther away an object is, the less apparent is its motion. The motions of eleven Cepheid variable stars were observed carefully, and when analyzed, the motions implied an average absolute magnitude of —2.4 for a variable star having a period of six days. Now Miss Leavitt had a standard for measuring distance and real magnitude.

When the period of change in brightness of a star is learned, we can apply the knowledge of this diagram to determine its absolute magnitude.

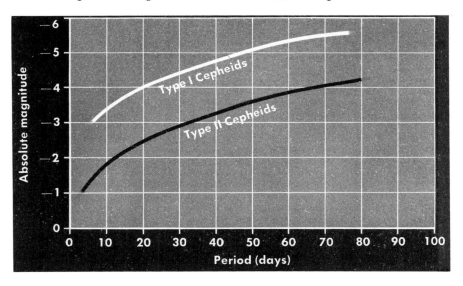

The curve showing relationships between periods and apparent magnitude indicated that a star with a period of six days would have an apparent magnitude of +14, so dim a powerful telescope is needed to detect it. Following the curve, one finds that an apparent magnitude of +15 gives an absolute magnitude of —1.4, and one with an apparent magnitude of +13 gives an absolute magnitude of —3.4.

Astronomers now had a way of determining vast distances with considerable accuracy. All they had to do was observe a Cepheid variable star long enough to determine its period. When that information was applied to the period-luminosity relationship, the absolute magnitude was known. And when one knows this, together with the apparent magnitude, distance can be computed.

When Cepheid variables were first studied, astronomers thought that all of them behaved in the same manner. They believed that all Cepheids with the same period must have the same absolute magnitude.

But there appear to be two different classes of Cepheids. Those of Type I are 1.5 magnitudes brighter than those of Type II, and their periods range from 1.5 to 40 days for Type I to 12 to 25 days for Type II.

In 1952 the fact that there were two different types of Cepheids was recognized when the 200-inch Hale telescope was turned on the Andromeda Galaxy. Certain variables which were thought to be short-period Cepheids failed to appear on the photographs. Since the stars were believed to be within the range of the photographic film being used, they must be dimmer than had been thought. There was something wrong with the distance scale arrived at by using the period-luminosity relationship. Agreement of the relationships with the facts revealed by the camera was attained by doubling the distance scale. This meant that in 1952, or shortly thereafter, man's conception of the size of the universe was doubled.

Astronomers strive continually to improve the accuracy of their knowledge. In measuring stellar distances, for example, the parallax method is used sometimes, at other times the inverse square law of light which uses real and apparent magnitudes. Also, ways of using the spectra of the stars as indicators of distance are often utilized. And there are other ways of determining stellar distances. Some of these are concerned with the motions of stars, the nature of space between the stars, the motion of our galaxy as a unit—some of which will be discussed in succeeding chapters.

But first let's consider the dilemma, in spite of the new knowledge about stellar distances and magnitudes, that men were having in understanding the nature of this galaxy in which we live—a galaxy of which we see only a small part, even when using the most powerful instruments, and which we comprehend only partially, even when our ingenuity and intellect are stretched to the utmost.

3

AN EMERGING UNDER-
STANDING OF THE
GALAXY

For a hundred years after Herschel had constructed his model of the universe, man's basic idea of the universe remained essentially unchanged. He still believed it was encompassed by the boundaries of our own galaxy, and there was nothing beyond. Considerable knowledge was obtained about the nature of the stars. For example, Bessel's technique for measuring distances was refined as observations became more precise. Relationships between stars were noted, and motions of stars were measured with accuracy, so Herschel's basic framework was fleshed out and refined. Also, observations had been made of nebulas of various shapes and sizes, some of them clearly spiral in nature.

Men knew that the galaxy was disk-shaped, as Thomas Wright had said it was, for Herschel had verified the beliefs of Thomas Wright by measuring the distribution of stars. Having little observational knowledge to cause them to think otherwise, men thought, for a century after they had conceived of our galaxy, that we were located at the center of it. This was, essentially, the belief that was advocated by the Dutch astronomer Jacobus C. Kapteyn (1851–1922) and which continued to be popular into this century. Just as Ptolemy's conception of the solar system (the universe of the ancients) put the earth at the center, so men of more recent times thought of our galaxy as a great disk of stars with the solar system at the center.

At the outset of the twentieth century, almost a hundred years after the death of William Herschel, men were not content to accept a superficial definition of the galaxy. They were groping for a fuller explanation of the place of the earth and the solar system in the scheme of the universe.

In 1920 a great debate was held in Washington, D.C., between two Americans: Harlow Shapley, an astronomer at the Mount Wilson Observatory, and Heber D. Curtis, an astronomer at the Lick Observatory. Both men had personally spent many years studying the arrangement of stars in the galaxy. But they had entirely different explanations for their observations.

The purpose of the debate was to explore the size of the Milky Way Galaxy and the structure of it. Related to this question was the nature of the great spiral formations that these men, as well as other astronomers, had observed and photographed. Were they part of our own galaxy, or objects outside the galaxy and at great distances from us?

Harlow Shapley had made careful studies of some ninety-three globular star clusters. Today we recognize over a hundred of these sphere-shaped clusters, some made of tens of thousands of stars,

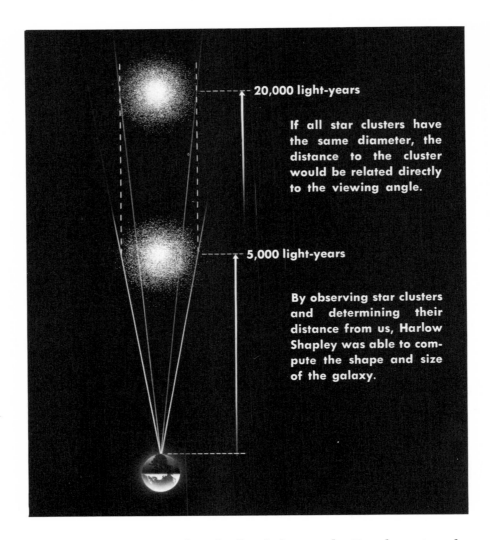

20,000 light-years

If all star clusters have the same diameter, the distance to the cluster would be related directly to the viewing angle.

5,000 light-years

By observing star clusters and determining their distance from us, Harlow Shapley was able to compute the shape and size of the galaxy.

and others containing hundreds of thousands. By observing the magnitude of certain variable stars within the globular clusters, Shapley could determine the distances to the stars and so to those clusters that contained the variable stars. Many globular clusters contain stars called RR Lyrae variables. These are stars that change from dim to bright in a short rhythmic interval. Their average absolute magnitude is seventy times that of the sun.

When a star is observed, we can determine its average apparent magnitude. Knowing the absolute and the apparent magnitudes, the distance to the star can be computed.

By extremely precise observations Shapley measured the observed diameters of globular clusters whose distance he had determined. Knowing the distance, he could then compute the true diameter of the cluster.

The next step was to assume that there was an average diameter for all clusters. A nearby cluster would seem to have a greater diameter than one far away because the size of an object appears to get smaller as distance becomes greater. By measuring how large the diameter seemed to be, he was able to make estimates of the distances to the clusters.

From knowledge of the directions of the globular clusters and their estimated distances, Shapley plotted their locations. He found that the ninety-three clusters that were known at that time formed a great ball-like, or spheroidal, formation, and that they were most dense toward their center. Having determined this much by actual observation, Shapley now made a bold step—and the one that many astronomers could not accept. He said the globular clusters were the "skeleton" of the galaxy. The center of the "ball" of globular clusters was 50,000 light-years from the solar system, and so the center of the galaxy must be 50,000 light-years from us. The direction of the center was toward the constellation Sagittarius. The entire galaxy, according to Shapley back in 1920, had a diameter of 300,000 light-years.

The solar system had lost the lofty central location given it by Thomas Wright, Herschel, and Kapteyn. It had been put off center. Shapley's figures for the size of the galaxy were high, according to present beliefs, because he did not consider the absorption of light by cosmic dust, which causes dimming of light. Currently, we believe that the diameter of the galaxy is closer to

100,000 light-years. However, this figure is quite uncertain because the galaxy has no sharp edge. There are investigators who believe Shapley's early estimate of 300,000 light-years may be the more accurate one if the distant spiral arms of the galaxy, the distant clusters, and the most remote gaseous clouds are considered.

Heber Curtis maintained that Shapley's measurements of the distances to the globular clusters were incorrect by a large factor. Curtis said, "I hold therefore to the belief that the Galaxy is probably not more than 30,000 light years in diameter." He was among the large number of astronomers who continued to believe that the solar system was at the center of the galaxy. Curtis and other astronomers also maintained strongly that "island universes," spiral formations that appeared cloudlike and which had been observed in large numbers, were actually huge formations of multitudes of stars. They thought the formations were galaxies outside our own. In the early 1920's Shapley believed the formations were not galaxies at all, but were concentrations of material inside our own galaxy.

Curtis was right in this part of the debate. Some of the formations—the nebulas—are inside our own galaxy. But vast numbers are truly other galaxies at great distances from our own. When this idea was accepted, knowledge of our own galaxy grew rapidly, for we could study entire galaxies outside our own. Much of what we learned about other galaxies provided answers to questions about our own galaxy.

The Shape and Size of the Galaxy

The center, or nucleus, of the galaxy is now believed to be 30,000 light-years from the sun. However, the uncertainty of the figure is high. It is wiser, and perhaps more accurate, to say that the center of the galaxy is somewhere between 25,000 and 35,000 light-years from the solar system.

We think the diameter of the galaxy is 100,000 light-years. But the reliability of this figure is not high either. The true diameter of the galaxy may be much greater. From top to bottom across the thickest part of the galaxy, the distance is about 15,000 light-years. As we proceed you will find how such conclusions are reached.

The main part of the galaxy is a wheel-shaped disk, a formation that is flattened as a result of its own rotation. However, the globular clusters, some 120 in number, appear to be arranged in a great sphere, having its center at the nucleus of the galactic disk. In addition, there appear to be separate and isolated stars distributed in a space that is roughly outlined by the positions of the clusters. The clusters and the "lone" stars together form what many astronomers believe is the galactic halo, a region that far exceeds the volume of the disk itself. In addition to isolated stars and clusters, the halo may contain small amounts of gases, for their presence is implied by radio emissions that are detected in the region.

Individual stars have been found as much as 50,000 light-years from the plane of the galaxy. This would mean the diameter of the halo would be at least 100,000 light-years. In rare cases, globular clusters seem to be a quarter of a million light-years away. Such clusters may belong to our galaxy or they may be disassociated from the galaxy, inhabitants of the immense reaches of intergalactic space. Judging by present observations, the halo appears to have a thickness of 100,000 light-years, and its diameter along the plane of the galactic disc may be 200,000 or even 300,000 light-years.

We believe that our galaxy is made up of some 100 billion stars; 100 or more star clusters move in orbits around the galaxy. The solar system is about two-thirds of the distance from the center, at the inside of a spiral arm.

The Number of Stars in the Galaxy

Two to three billion stars appear on photographs taken with the largest optical telescopes. This means that the images are so crowded that ten thousand stars may be found within a circle on the photograph having a diameter of one half of one degree, the diameter of the full moon against the sky background. Although the stars on such photographs appear very close together, they are separated actually by distances measured in light-years. Suppose a model of the galaxy were constructed to a scale in which the size of an average star could be represented by a raindrop. The distance between raindrops would have to be about forty miles to give a valid idea of the actual distances between stars. For every cubic inch of stellar material in the galaxy there are about 10^{22} cubic inches of empty space. (The number 10^{22} means the number 10 raised to the 22nd power, or the number 1 followed by 22 zeros; thus 10,000,000,000,000,000,000,000.)

The distant stars, and even the very faint nearby ones, cannot be photographed, and so another method is required to determine the total number of stars there are in the galaxy. We can get an approximation of the total by finding the mass of the galaxy, and how it compares with the mass of a typical star.

Shapley and others have established that the sun is about 30,-000 light-years from the center of the galaxy. This is equivalent to 10,000 parsecs. (An object having a *par*allax of one *sec*ond, would be at a distance of 1 parsec, or 3.26 light-years.) If the galaxy were circular, then the distance around it, or circumference, at the location of the sun, can be found as follows:

$$
\begin{aligned}
\text{Circumference} &= 2\pi \times \text{radius} \\
&= 2 \times 3.1416 \times 10,000 \text{ parsecs} \\
&= 62,832 \text{ parsecs}
\end{aligned}
$$

If we can find how fast the sun is moving around the center of the galaxy, we can determine the time required for one complete journey. When astronomers study the light given off by distant stars in the direction of the constellation Cygnus, they find that there is a shift of spectral lines toward the blue. A blue shift, one where the spectral lines are all shifted toward the blue, or short-wave, end of the spectrum, indicates motion toward the observer. The amount of shift indicates that the stars are moving toward us at about two hundred miles per second—or that we are moving toward them at the same velocity.

We know that all stars have motions of their own, but the fact that the spectral lines of all the stars in one direction show a blue shift, while those in the opposite direction show a red shift or movement away from the observer, can only be interpreted as results of our own motion. We are moving toward Cygnus at a velocity of some two hundred miles a second in a great orbit around the center of the galaxy.

Observations of the shifts of the spectral lines of the light of globular clusters lead to a similar conclusion.

We know that the circumference of the galaxy at the location of the sun is 62,832 parsecs, and now we have determined that the velocity is 200 miles a second. If you work out the arithmetic, you'll find this means that the time required for the galaxy to complete one rotation at the distance of the sun is 200,000,000 years (2×10^8 years).

To go farther in our computations, we shall have to disregard all matter in the galaxy that is farther from the center than the sun is. Also, we must assume that all of the mass of the galaxy is concentrated at the center of the galaxy. Once we've made these two assumptions we can regard the sun and the galaxy as two bodies revolving around one another.

The next step is to apply Kepler's third law to the problem.

Johannes Kepler, the German astronomer and mathematician, determined through careful study of tables of planetary positions and motions that the squares of the periods of planets (or other bodies) are equal to the cubes of their distances ($p^2 = d^3$).

Later on Sir Isaac Newton modified Kepler's third law enabling mass to be found. By supplying to the relationships the figures we have obtained, we can now determine the mass of the galaxy. You remember that we had the distance of the sun from the center of the galaxy as 10,000 parsecs. In our computation we must change this measurement to astronomical units—the mean distance 92,900,000 miles between the earth and sun. In one parsec there are 200,000 astronomical units (2×10^5). Therefore, in 10,000 parsecs (1×10^4) there would be (2×10^5) $\times$ (1×10^4), or 2×10^9 astronomical units. (To multiply powers of ten, you simply add the exponents.)

The mass of the sun compared to the mass of the galaxy is so small it can be disregarded. We find that:

$$\text{mass of the galaxy} = \frac{\text{distance}^3}{\text{period}^2}$$

$$= \frac{(2 \times 10^9)^3}{(2 \times 10^8)^2}$$

$$= \frac{8 \times 10^{27}}{4 \times 10^{16}}$$

$$= 2 \times 10^{11}$$

When you divide the powers of ten, you simply subtract the exponents. The mass of the galaxy is 2×10^{11}, 200 billion times the mass of the sun. The galaxy appears to be made of about 200 billion stars—assuming that the mass of the sun is average. This figure does not consider the stars and gases that are farther

Isaac Newton (1642-1727), English astronomer-mathematician who propounded the law of universal gravitation.

H. K WIMMER

from the center of the galaxy than is the sun, and so the actual number of stars in the galaxy may be much higher, according to this procedure.

Estimates of the number of stars in the galaxy may be made in another way, by reverting to star counts, much as Herschel did, though in a more refined manner. Another way is to use simple arithmetic: divide the number of stars there are in a given volume of space into the total volume of the galaxy. Astronomers have determined that the number density of stars is 0.14 per cubic parsec in the vicinity of the sun. (A cubic parsec would be a cube measuring 3.26 light-years along each edge.)

Now let's see if we can get some idea of the volume of the galaxy. Since most of the stars are in the galactic disk, we'll find the volume of a disk with a radius of 15,000 parsecs and one that is 1,000 parsecs thick. This thickness should provide for the greater density of stars at the galactic center and for the smaller number in the halo. When you do the arithmetic, divide the volume of the galaxy by 0.14 (the number of the stars in one cubic parsec). The answer will be very close to 1×10^{11} stars.

The number of stars in our galaxy is probably somewhat more than 100 billion stars, and somewhat less than 150 billion. There is as much variety among these billions of stars as among the leaves of the trees. Stars vary in color and brightness, in age and composition, in size and density.

As the entomologist finds it helpful to classify insects according to certain characteristics, so the astronomer defines his studies by placing a star in a group or class according to its characteristics. Two extremely broad classifications are called Population One and Population Two. The classification was devised by Walter Baade, an astronomer who came to the United States from Germany.

Population One stars may be of many different ages, including stars that have been formed recently or may actually be in the process of formation. Such stars are associated with the spiral arms of the galaxy and with the gas and dust patches in the galaxy. Population Two stars are those that are very old, maybe so old that they were formed at the time of the creation of the galaxy, and are located in the nucleus of the galaxy, in the globular clusters, and in the halo. Most stars found at locations other than the spiral arms are included under Population Two.

Variation Among the Stars

The diversity of stars is so great that two large groups cannot alone serve to classify them in a logical, usable fashion. Astronomers have devised many different ways of grouping stars, making comparisons possible and enabling inferences to be made. One way is by the color and brightness of a star.

In the early part of this century Ejnar Hertzsprung, a Danish astronomer, studied the color and brightness of stars in clusters. He constructed charts showing that stars of certain colors had certain degrees of brightness. At nearly the same time the American astronomer Henry N. Russell was making a study of the stars in the neighborhood of the sun. He was comparing their colors (spectral classes) with their absolute magnitudes—how bright they would be if placed at the standard distance of 10 parsecs (32.6 light-years). Out of these investigations grew the H-R diagram (the Hertzsprung-Russell diagram), which has proved extremely valuable in organizing stars, finding relationships between them, determining relative distances, compositions, degrees of brightness.

Careful determination of the color of a star enables the astron-

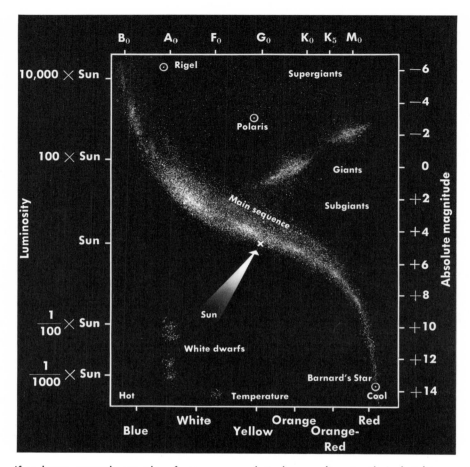

If a large enough sample of stars were plotted according to their brightness and color, they would fall into a pattern like this one. It is called the Hertz-sprung-Russell diagram after the men mostly responsible for its development.

omer to place it in a class according to its color. The blue-white stars, which are extremely rare, are called O stars; those that are a bit whiter and cooler are classified as B stars. As the color changes to yellow-white, yellow, yellow-orange, orange, and so on to dull red, the classifications change. The various groupings are O, B, A, F, G, K, M. Such an incongruous array of letters needs an explanation. When stars were first classified, they were as-

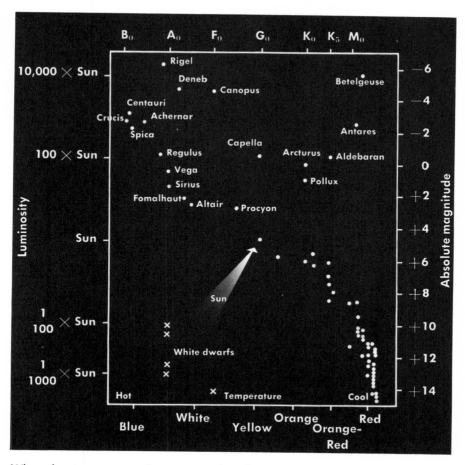

When the stars nearest the sun are plotted on an H-R diagram, we see a preponderance at the red end of the diagram; bright stars are rarities.

signed the letters of the alphabet, A, B, C, and so on, in order of temperatures as they were believed to be. As more was learned about the behavior of gases at high temperatures, it was found that stars originally labeled O were actually the brightest and hottest stars. Originally they had been placed far along in the alphabet because all of the O stars are distant and therefore dim.

The O stars were placed at the top of the list. Next were the

B stars, then the A stars, which originally had been at the top. The arrangement and order of the dark lines in the spectra of stars were keys to classification. Study of these lines determined that stars originally classified as F should be next after A. Then came stars originally classified G, K, and M in that order. To remember the order of stars by temperature, from the very hot to the very cool, simply remember: "Oh, Be A Fine Girl, Kiss Me."

From experience in the laboratory with gases and solids, we also know that colors change with changes in temperature. When a material is very hot, the color becomes blue-white. As the material cools, the color becomes more yellowish; then it changes to orange, and ultimately to dull brick-red. Therefore, once the color of a star is known, we also know its temperature. Notice that along the horizontal scale of the H-R diagram we may put spectral class, or temperature. Another measure that we can use is color index.

The color index is just a second way of describing the color of a star, and it is obtained by subtracting the photovisual magnitude from the photographic magnitude of a star. When a star is photographed with a film that is especially sensitive to blue light, the magnitude of the image obtained is called the photographic magnitude of the star. When the star is photographed with a film that has about the same response as the human eye, the magnitude is called photovisual. A very blue star (a hot one such as Rigel in Orion) appears brighter on blue-sensitive film than on film that has a response similar to the human eye. For example, a star might have a magnitude of $+2.6$ (photographic) and $+3.0$ (photovisual). When we subtract $+3.0$ from $+2.6$, we have an answer of -0.4. This will be the color index of the star. It can be seen, then, that color indexes tell us something about the temperature of the star, as well as its color. This is why the horizontal scale can be given in units of spectral class, temperature, or color index. The factor more commonly used today is color index.

We can take each star for which we know a distance and compute its absolute magnitude. For each of these stars we can determine a color index. Then if we plot absolute magnitude against color index we can form a diagram, just as Hertzsprung and Russell did. And the curious thing is that stars do not fall on all parts of the diagram, but just in certain particular regions. This means that, while stars do vary a great deal in a multitude of characteristics, such as size, brightness, color and temperature, the variations fall within rather fixed boundaries.

Hot, bright stars are located at the upper left part of the diagram, and cool, dim stars are at the lower right.

A star that is very cool but very bright, such as Antares in Scorpio, will fall somewhere in the upper right portion of the diagram. In order for a star to be very cool but also very bright, it must be very large. Such stars are called giants or supergiants.

Most of the stars in the vicinity of the sun—that is, in one of the spiral arms of the galaxy—will fall somewhere along a smooth shallow S curve that extends from the upper left of the diagram to the lower right. Since most stars fall on this curve, it is called the main sequence of stars. In the immediate area of the sun there are no giant stars and about 10 percent of them are dwarfs, and so an H-R diagram of those particular stars—the stars within 5 parsecs, let us say—is quite different from a diagram that includes stars at greater distances.

From the H-R diagram one can see that when certain characteristics of a star are determined, other conditions can be surmised. For example, suppose we have determined that a star has a color index of +0.5 and an absolute magnitude of —5. We know immediately that it has a temperature a bit less than 5,000 degrees Kelvin (this is the scale that gives a positive value to all temperature measurements—absolute zero being 0 degrees Kelvin and zero degrees centigrade being +273 degrees Kelvin). We know also that the star is dull yellow in color, and it is about ten thousand times brighter than the sun. The star must be a supergiant.

The sun is a G_2 star. Its absolute magnitude is +4.84; its color index +0.6. It is a yellow star, and it is on the main sequence.

Giant stars such as the one referred to above have very low densities. While their volume may be several million times the volume of the sun, they are made up of only fifty or so times more material than is contained in the sun. While huge stars such as this are extremely rare, you can see one in Orion. It is Betelgeuse, which seems to have a diameter that changes, as the star pulsates, from some 700 million to 1,000 million miles.

Betelgeuse, a supergiant star, is red in color, which means its temperature is low. However, not all red, cool stars are large. Take another look at the H-R diagram and notice that stars located at the lower right of the main sequence are also cool, red stars. These stars shine dimly—they have a high absolute magnitude. In order for such a star to shine so dimly, the star must be very small. Some of them have diameters of only 100,000 miles, or sometimes less. Even though these main-sequence stars are cool, red, and small, they still contain a large amount of material, making their densities very high.

If you study the H-R diagram you'll notice that dwarf stars are represented in the lower left area. Since they are toward the left, you know the stars must be very hot. Most very hot stars are also very bright. But the dwarfs are near the bottom of the chart, indicating that they are dim stars. If they are hot but dim, they must be very small.

Only a few dwarf stars can be observed. They have diameters of only three thousand miles, or even less. Yet these stars contain vast amounts of materials that are packed tightly together, raising the density to levels that we cannot comprehend. For example, it is not unusual for a dwarf star to have a density 200,000 times greater than the density of water. In terms of weight—a pint of water weighs about one pound—a pint of the material a white dwarf is made of would weigh some 200,000 pounds, or 100 tons.

The Milky Way Galaxy contains billions of stars of all varieties. There are main-sequence stars, red giants, white dwarfs. There are stars of different sizes and brightnesses, stars that eclipse one another, stars that explode and disappear. Also, there are new stars, for stars seem to form continually from the great masses of gases that abound in the plane of the galaxy.

The Nebulas

Not all of the material in our galaxy is in the form of stars. Most of it is, but about 2 or 3 percent is in the form of gas and dust between the stars. Sometimes, when the physical conditions are just right, the gaseous matter will emit light and be visible as a bright fuzzy patch on the sky. These are the nebulas that were catalogued by Charles Messier, the French astronomer. Often the gaseous matter is observable as a dark region, because starlight behind it is scattered and not observable from the earth. Astronomers can classify different types of nebulas, and we will describe a few of the more common types.

Ionization Nebulas

Just below the easternmost two of the three belt stars of the constellation Orion lies a bright nebula of great interest. The formation can be seen with binoculars. Its dimensions are of the order of a few parsecs, and its mass is as great as several thousand suns. It becomes dramatic when observed through a low-power telescope and is a beautiful array of reds and yellows when photographed in color, using a long time exposure.

Most of the gas in the galaxy is cold hydrogen that produces no light. There are usually only a few atoms per cubic centimeter, but occasionally the number jumps to a thousand or more in the same volume. When such densities are reached and when the gases are in the vicinity of stars so energetic that most of the radiation they give off is in the ultraviolet range, a spectacular nebula results. This is what happens in the bright nebula of Orion.

Stars in the region give off ultraviolet radiation, which is absorbed by the hydrogen atoms. The atom becomes a free proton (nucleus of one atom) and a free electron. The different particles fly around free of one another. The protons collide with other electrons and each captures one of them. The electron, once captured, moves from one position in the atom to another, releasing energy at each step. The energy is in the form of visible light.

As soon as such a series is begun, additional bombardment by ultraviolet radiation causes another separation of the proton and electron, and so the release-and-capture sequence continues.

The process is very much like that which operates in fluorescent lamps. Ultraviolet radiation produced by the excited gas in the tube strikes the inner wall of the tube, which is coated with a phosphor. The ultraviolet radiation causes the atoms in the phosphor to lose electrons, which are then free to move about. When the electrons are captured, they move from one shell of the atom to another, releasing energy in the form of visible light as each step is completed.

The bright ionization nebula in Orion reradiates energy received from nearby stars.

A Reflection Nebula

The next time you're observing the Pleiades in the constellation of Taurus, take a close look. Observe the region with a telescope if you can. The entire area seems to be aglow.

The casual observer sees six stars in the Pleiades—but when the cluster is observed more carefully, seven can be seen, and with a telescope scores can be detected. The total number is probably five hundred or so, making this group one of the best known of all the open clusters of stars.

Space abounds not only with gases but also with interstellar dust. Occasionally this dust catches the light of nearby stars and reflects the light to us. Such is the case around the bright stars in

Formations of gases in the Pleiades reflect light from nearby stars.

The Pleiades are in Taurus, just west of Orion, and also slightly west of the bright star Aldebaran.

the Pleiades cluster. We cannot exaggerate the beauty of the Pleiades when they are seen telescopically. At the top of the group one sees the bright star Atlas and its fainter companion Pleione. The great central star is Alcyone, and just below this star and on the sides left and right are Merope and Maia, which are imbedded in glowing gases. The very bright star centered just below and also in a haze of light is Electra. The seventh member of the group is Taygeta, below and to the right of Maia.

A Radio Nebula

In the constellation Taurus, just to the north of Orion, there is another interesting formation of gases known as the Crab Nebula because of its sprawling, crablike appearance when viewed through a telescope.

In 1054 the Chinese reported that there was a great burst of light in this part of the sky—an exploding star. During the centuries since then, the gases ejected by that star have been moving away from the central region at a speed of 750 miles per second.

This high velocity, or more accurately other mechanisms that are not presently comprehended but which appear to be related to velocity, causes the Crab Nebula to be a source of strong radio waves. The nature of the radio waves causes astronomers to suspect that the waves are related to electrons spiraling at high speeds along magnetic lines of force. Radiation produced in this

63

The Crab Nebula in Taurus is made up of gases that were consolidated in a star that exploded about 1,000 years ago.

fashion is called synchroton radiation because similar radiation is produced by electrons as they are accelerated in a synchroton —a type of nuclear accelerator.

Not only are radio waves produced by this sort of action, but certain wavelengths of light are produced at the same time. Presently, it is generally accepted that the light of the Crab Nebula, or at least a large part of it, is produced by electrons moving rapidly along magnetic lines of force. Although this explanation is accepted, the sources of neither the electrons nor the lines of force have been explained adequately.

Dark Nebulas

Not all nebulas are observable because of their brightness. Quite the contrary, there are nebulas which can be seen only in silhouette; great masses of dark material seen by contrast against a bright background. Perhaps the most well known of all dark nebulas is the beautiful Horsehead Nebula in Orion.

Insterstellar space abounds with gases and cosmic dust. Just as there are regions where the gases are more densely assembled than normally, so also there are regions where the cosmic dust is more dense than in the immensity of space as a whole. But even in the darkest clouds there are still great distances between the particles. However, the clouds of particles occupy tremendous

The dark Horsehead Nebula in Orion is silhouetted against bright stars and gases that lie at greater distances.

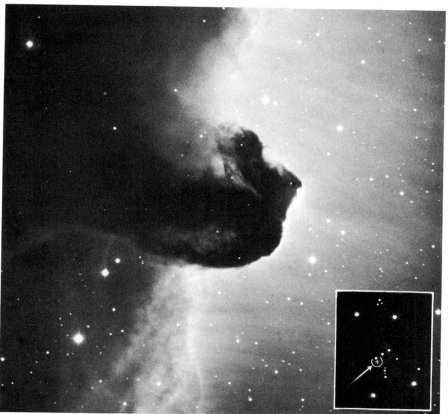

volumes having diameters that are measured in light-years, and so the light of stars that lie beyond is dissipated and we cannot see it.

The part of the dark nebula that produces the head of the horse, and the region at the left, is composed of cosmic dust many light-years in thickness. The bright stars at the far left of the photograph are closer to us than the cosmic dust. And the bright region against which the horse's head is silhouetted is much more distant than the dark, obscuring material.

Globules in Nebulas

In addition to the dark nebula in Orion, the Milky Way itself abounds with dark, obscuring regions. The next time you have a clear, dark summer sky, look along the Milky Way. You will see bright areas. But you will also see dark regions which at first look like great cavernous openings to the blackness of space. Actually, these regions are masses of cosmic dust so extensive that the light of the stars that lie beyond is obscured. Often the amount of darkening is severe. In the region of Aquila, the Eagle, which can be seen in our summer skies, the darkening causes a drop of 1.1 magnitudes, and in the direction of Ophiuchus, the Serpent Bearer, a bit to the west of Aquila, it amounts to 3.5 magnitudes and accounts for the relative obscurity of the constellation.

While these extensive areas of dark material are of great interest, many astronomers have also been concerned in recent years about extremely limited concentrations of obscuring material, such as those which appear in the photograph of the nebula Messier 8 in Sagittarius.

These dark regions are often circular, though not always, and are relatively very small. When seen in the direction of the center of the galaxy they may be only one-half light-year in diameter.

The Lagoon Nebula in Sagittarius (Messier 8) is a mass of gases in which new stars (a few of which are indicated by the arrows) are being created.

In the opposite direction the dimensions are two to four times greater. The larger clouds are rather transparent, and there seems to be a steady increase in opaqueness as the cloud becomes more concentrated.

Many astronomers feel that these "globules" are stars in the process of formation. They have good reason to believe that radiant energy from nearby stars pushes the gases into more and more compact masses. Once the process is initiated, the gravitational attraction of the gases themselves causes further accretion, and also a steady and rapid increase in temperature.

It is entirely feasible and plausible to believe that the process can continue until the conditions of mass, pressure, and temperature have reached those levels that are needed in order for a given collection of materials to become a star—a mass that converts part of its own substance into energy and so becomes self-sustaining.

And so our galaxy is immense, dynamic, studded with stars both old and new. As Galileo said so eloquently in 1610 about the broad belt of stars that reaches across our sky from horizon to horizon: "the Galaxy is nothing else but a vast conjury of stars planted together in clusters . . . the number is quite beyond determination."

But Galileo was describing the Milky Way (the universe of those times) from a perspective that was limited by a minimum of actual observation and by the slim total knowledge of his time.

Indeed, very likely such is the case even today when astronomers explain the nature of our galaxy.

Today we conceive of our galaxy as being composed of billions of isolated star clusters and star groups, and vast volumes of gases, some extremely nebulous, others densely concentrated. But this conception may change as better instruments and techniques are developed. All we can do is report on our observations and interpret them, using the knowledge presently available.

As years pass by man improves his technology; he "sees" farther and better, and so new areas in the universe are exposed, demanding new and different interpretations. For example, in the 1940's radio astronomy began to develop rapidly. Now it has become a robust field of investigation, one that has sustained the knowledge about the galaxy that had been obtained largely through investigations with optical telescopes. But more than simply bolstering information already assembled, radio astronomy has revealed new and exciting horizons, as we shall find in the next chapter.

4

EXPLORING BY RADIO

BEFORE THE days of radio astronomy all observations made by astronomers since the beginning of time had been in the optical, or visible-light, range of the electromagnetic spectrum. Information was obtained by viewing through one window alone, and a window that had many limitations.

In the 1940's men "saw" an entirely new view of the universe when astronomers turned to radio astronomy, a new and exciting field of investigation.

All of us know something about optical astronomy, for we experience aspects of it all through our lives whenever we look at the sky. But radio astronomy is not as well understood. In order to understand how this "new astronomy" affected our ideas concerning the structure and motions of our galaxy, it is necessary to know something about radio astronomy—what it is, why it functions, its limitations. We'll explore these questions briefly.

The first thinking about radio astronomy occurred in 1890, when physicists worked out the theory of radiation. Among other

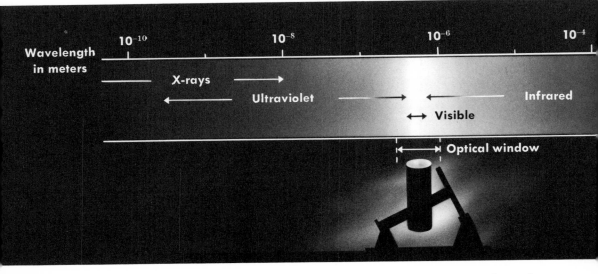

| Wavelength in meters | 10^{-10} | | 10^{-8} | | 10^{-6} | | 10^{-4} |

X-rays

Ultraviolet

Infrared

Visible

Optical window

Energy radiates from the sun and other stars in wavelengths ranging from ultra-short to very long. Altogether, the radiation comprises the electromagnetic

conditions, this theory held that waves are radiated from stars at all different energy levels, and not only in the form of heat and light. Waves of radiant energy—all of which travel at some 186,000 miles per second—range from the extremely short waves (the gamma rays) to the extremely long waves (the long-wave radio waves). Here we show the gamut of radiant energy with the optical window indicated. This is the radiation which comes to us as visible light. As any sky watcher knows, no matter how casual he may be, the optical window is often blocked by clouds, smoke, haze, thermals, or simply a murky and dusty atmosphere. There are serious and confounding limitations to observations by optical telescopes.

The radio window is also indicated in the diagram. Radio waves can penetrate smoke, haze, and weather. They can be "observed" in daylight as well as in darkness, and they can penetrate haze and dust through which light cannot possibly pass.

70

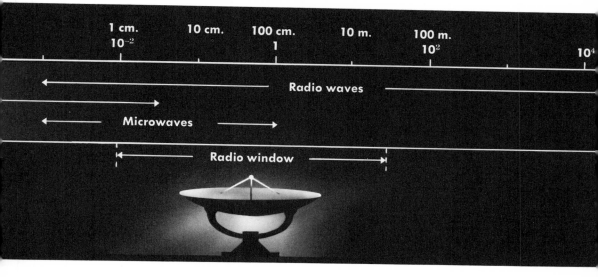

| 1 cm. 10^{-2} | 10 cm. | 100 cm. 1 | 10 m. | 100 m. 10^2 | 10^4 |

Radio waves

Microwaves

Radio window

spectrum. Astronomers gather information using instruments sensitive to various wavelengths.

In the latter part of the 1890's attempts were made to pick up radio waves which many physicists theorized must be generated in the sun and in other stars. But the attempts were not successful, because at that time equipment was not sensitive to weak impulses. In the early decades of the 1900's, much better equipment for receiving and amplifying radio waves was built, but somehow no one felt inclined to explore radio waves in outer space. In fact, even in 1932 when they were finally investigated, the study was incidental to other and more pressing requirements.

In 1932 Karl G. Jansky, an electronics engineer, was working at the Bell Telephone Laboratories at Holmdel, New Jersey. His task was to find the reasons why long-distance radio-telephonic communications were disrupted at rather regular intervals. Jansky designed a radio antenna to determine the direction and arrival of radio noise—energy that sounds like static when we pick it up on our ordinary home receivers. He reported:

71

> The first complete record obtained showed the surprising
> fact that the . . . direction of arrival of these waves changed
> nearly 360 degrees in 24 hours . . . . These facts lead to the
> conclusion that the direction of arrival of the waves re-
> mains fixed in space . . . .

Jansky knew that somehow the radio noise he was receiving
was connected with the broad belt of stars, the Milky Way, that
extended around the sky, because the noise recurred when the
Milky Way was in the field of the instruments. And the noise
probably came from the most dense region of the Milky Way.
Jansky's investigations were released to the world in 1933.

Although there were exceptions, most astronomers in the 1930's
gave little attention to the work of Karl Jansky. Very likely, part
of the indifference of astronomers was due to their ignorance of
radio and its implications. And, although one does not relish
admitting it, part of the indifference was no doubt due to reluc-
tance to accept ideas that were new and revolutionary. Ever since
the birth of astronomy all observations had been made optically.
Jansky's report, if valid, would change the science of astronomy,
opening up horizons unsuspected except by a small handful of
pioneers.

The next great step in radio astronomy, ironically enough, was
made not by an astronomer but by a radio engineer, apparently
the only person who appreciated Jansky's discovery enough to be
challenged to investigate it further. Grote Reber was this inquisi-
tive radio engineer. In the middle of the 1930's Reber built the
first parabolic reflector (radio dish) near his home in Wheaton,
Illinois. The dish could be swung up and down to view objects
in the sky at different altitudes.

Jansky is usually credited with the discovery of radio astronomy
and of the fact that the center of the galaxy, the region toward

the constellation Sagittarius, produces discernible radio noise. However, Grote Reber made gigantic strides in the science. He discovered that the sun gave off faint radio emissions. According to Reber, the level of emission from the sun is very small compared with that of the central region of the galaxy—a fact that has been verified over and over again since the thirties. For normal stars like the sun, the radiation in the radio band is so small that we cannot observe it at the distance of the stars. However, under certain conditions of temperature, density, and magnetic field, strong radiation is emitted in the radio range. Reber found discrete objects other than stars that were giving off radio energy. Some of these are the wisps of gas in the area of Cassiopeia, the so-called colliding galaxies in Cygnus, the emission nebula in Orion.

Reber's work influenced many astronomers in the United States and in other parts of the world. However, in the early 1940's, with the coming of the Second World War, it became necessary for all such studies to be put aside until hostilities were terminated.

Nevertheless, considerable progress in radio astronomy was made during the war. Radar, which makes use of reflected radio waves, was brought to a high degree of sensitivity. The techniques necessary to radar were immediately transferable to radio astronomy. Therefore, the field moved ahead rapidly after 1945 when the war ended.

As our galaxy was explored by radio astronomers, a picture quite different from that revealed by optical telescopes evolved. Here—completely invisible to the eye—were formations whose existence could be known only because radio waves that they were emitting were received by the antennas.

To understand why the picture looks so different to the radio receivers, you should turn back to the H-R diagram. You will see that an average star like the sun lies just about in the center of the color axis. The sun is a yellow star, and our eyes are most sensitive to light of this wavelength. But astronomers now understand that there are many, many types of objects in the galaxy that lie off the range of this color axis. Off the diagram to the left is the ultraviolet region. Stars that radiate most of their energy in this range would not be detectable at the surface of the earth, for our atmosphere does not transmit the ultraviolet. However, balloons and rockets and satellites, and even astronauts, have photographed the sky in the ultraviolet region, and many exciting discoveries are being made.

Still farther to the left is the X-ray region. Rockets with X-ray detectors have located regions of intense X-ray emission, and astronomers are now identifying these regions with stars that appear very undistinguished in the optical region. For reasons not yet understood, some apparently normal stars are radiating most of their energy in the X-ray region.

And the story is similar in the infrared region and the radio region off to the right of the H-R diagram. Objects whose existence was never before imagined are being detected in the infrared and the radio regions.

Most of these exciting developments have come about because modern engineering has made it possible to construct sensitive detectors. Astronomers now realize that they can gather information in all regions of the spectrum. The important thing is that radio astronomy provides us with additional information about the sun and about our galaxy which, we hope, will lead to greater understanding.

From our location in the galaxy, when we look along the plane of the Milky Way, we can see optically only the nearby stars.

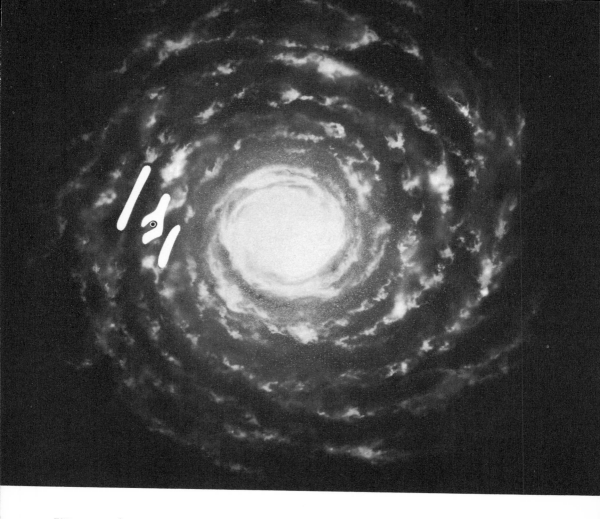

We can observe, with the unaided eye, stars in this diagram only in the small circle centered on the sun. The center of our galaxy and stars on the other side are hidden behind gas and dust. After years of investigation, and after hundreds of photographs of the stars were taken, artists drew the galaxy shown on page 76. It shows very well that the stars are concentrated along the plane of the galaxy. As we move away from the plane, both north and south, the frequency of occurrence of stars drops off rapidly, and there is only a little gas and dust.

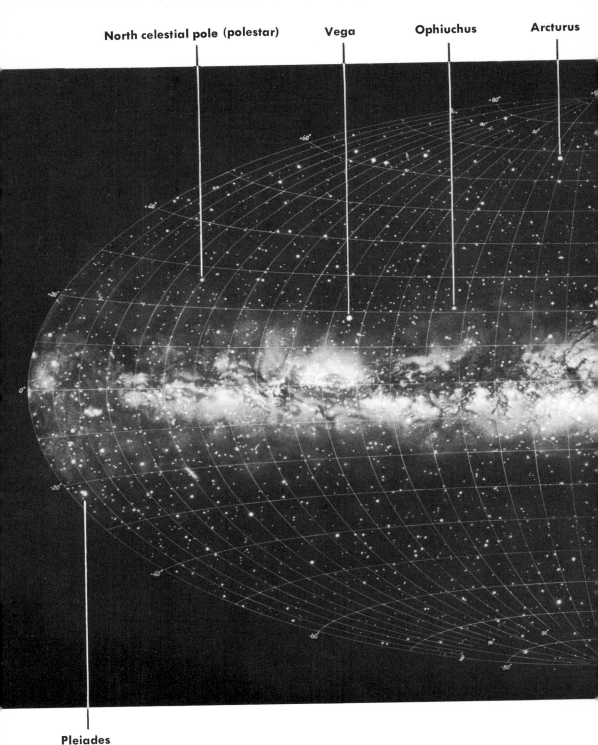

North celestial pole (polestar)

Vega

Ophiuchus

Arcturus

Pleiades

This panorama of our galaxy contains 7,000 stars accurately placed, and the
Milky Way painted in on the basis of photographs. Many persons are respon-

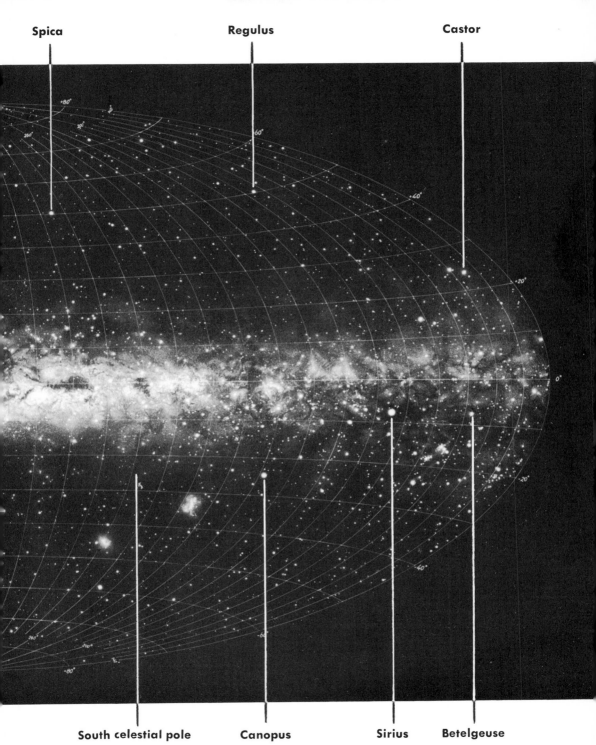

Spica Regulus Castor

South celestial pole Canopus Sirius Betelgeuse

sible for this fine rendition, especially Knut Lundmark, Martin and Tatjana Kesküla, and, of course, the Lund, Sweden, Observatory.

Here is a map representing a radio survey of the same region. The radio energy is especially strong where the lines are close together. Just as the artist's painting is whiter where there is more light, the lines of equal radio energy are closer where the energy is greater. The greatest radio energy comes from the region toward the center of the galaxy—and the level fades off rapidly as

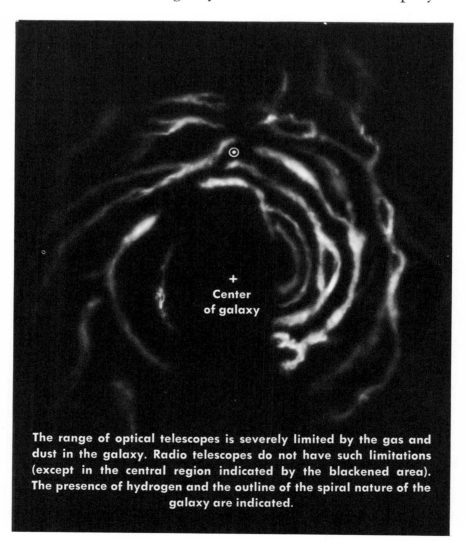

+
Center
of galaxy

The range of optical telescopes is severely limited by the gas and dust in the galaxy. Radio telescopes do not have such limitations (except in the central region indicated by the blackened area). The presence of hydrogen and the outline of the spiral nature of the galaxy are indicated.

one moves away from the central region. Radio waves are not stopped by the gaseous matter that lies between the stars because the length of radio waves is much greater than the cross section of the particles themselves. Therefore the radio telescope, quite unlike the optical instruments, can "see" right through to the edge of the galaxy. Notice that, even though there is a concentration of radio energy along the plane of the galaxy, the level of radio energy does not drop off as rapidly as does light energy as we move north and south away from the plane. This implies to some astronomers that our galaxy is imbedded in a spherical formation of material that emits radio waves energetically. Perhaps our radio galaxy is indeed a sphere, rather than a flattened spiral as it is usually represented.

Hydrogen 21-Centimeter Radiation

In the early days of radio astronomy, a few sources of radio waves could be located accurately. But the information was blurred because it was being received in a variety of wavelengths. In optical astronomy, we can filter out certain wavelengths, and so explore a light source in only a single wavelength at a time. In 1951 we learned how to do effectively the same thing with radio waves.

Seven years earlier, in 1944, the Dutch astronomer H. C. van de Hulst predicted that the cold hydrogen gas in interstellar space should be detectable. Furthermore he said the radiation would have a wavelength of 21 centimeters, or a frequency of 1420.4057 megacycles. If this hydrogen radiation could be observed, then it would be possible to construct a map of the galaxy in that wavelength, just as a galaxy could be constructed in the wavelengths of visible light. The hydrogen could not be identified until sensitive radio receivers were developed, since the total radio energy received by all the radio receivers in the world amounts to less than one erg. (That is less than the energy needed to make a mosquito airborne.) The radio energy itself arises as the electron of the hydrogen atom reverses its spin, as described below.

The hydrogen atom is made of a proton, which carries a positive charge, and an electron, which carries a negative charge. The electron moves in an orbit around the proton, much as the earth moves around the sun. However, the electron is not in a fixed orbit. Under certain conditions it can jump from one location to another. If energy is available to the atom, the electron absorbs energy and so moves into an orbit farther from the proton. Should the electron move into an orbit closer to the proton, energy is given off. The energy will be in definite amounts and frequencies. If the amount of energy is small, the frequency will be low and in the form of radio waves, heat, or light. If the amount of energy is high, the frequency will be high and in the form of ultraviolet radiation or X-rays.

The electrons of the hydrogen atoms in space do not jump from orbit to orbit. There is not enough energy for that to happen. Extremely small and fine adjustments are made by the electron within a given orbit. The adjustment we are concerned with is the flip-over of the electron. Both the proton and the electron are spinning. At intervals of some 10 million years for an average atom, the spin of the electron reverses. This results in the ejection of a small bundle of energy at a frequency of 1420.4057 megacycles (21 centimeters).

Immediately after the 21-centimeter line of hydrogen was predicted, astronomers in Holland and Australia looked for, and found, it. However, they found that the radiation was not always exactly 1420.4057 megacycles. They found three hydrogen signals that were as much as 200 kilocycles (thousand cycles) apart, even though they were along a single line of sight. Probably, the telescope was "looking" at several different hydrogen clouds moving at different speeds.

If a hydrogen atom is stationary, the radiation it emits will be very nearly 1,420 megacycles. However, if the atom is moving toward us, the radiation will be shifted just a bit higher, and if the atom is moving away from us, the radiation will be shifted just a bit lower. This is called the Doppler shift.

By detecting the 21-centimeter line of hydrogen, and by determining its precise frequency, the astronomer can learn a great deal about the galaxy. He can map the distribution of the gas in the galaxy, and by noting slight shifts in the frequency, he can determine whether the gas is moving toward us or away from us, and how fast it is moving.

Information about the galaxy, as presented in chapter 3, was gathered primarily by optical telescopes. But the optical telescope has severe limitations. For example, light cannot penetrate the thick and dark clouds that abound in certain parts of the galaxy. Indeed, so prevalent are these clouds that only about one-twentieth of the galaxy can be seen with optical telescopes.

But these clouds do not hamper the "view" of radio telescopes any more than weather clouds here on the earth interfere with radio communication. Radio astronomy opens up the entire galaxy to our perusal, permitting a view into the very center of it.

In radio astronomy when we say we can "see" or "view" a region we do not mean in the literal sense. Rather, we mean that we can pick up radio energy and so obtain knowledge of the manner in which the material that produces the radio waves is distributed. The Doppler shift, for example, tells us that the galaxy is moving, and the velocity of its motion.

In the illustration on page 78 we show the spiral arms of the galaxy as determined by radio telescopes. The gases to the right of the sun exhibit a Doppler shift toward the blue, or shorter wavelengths, indicating motion toward us or our motion toward the gases. The gases to the left exhibit a red shift, which is interpreted as a movement away from us or our motion away from the gases. Notice that the region of the galaxy opposite to the location of the sun is black. No movements can be detected there, and we presume that the gases must be moving across the "line of sight," neither toward us nor away from us.

Radio noise emanates from the direction of the center of the galaxy. The information indicates that hydrogen gas is flowing outward from the center of the galaxy, and in the plane of the galaxy.

When the radio galaxy is mapped at different wavelengths, the maps differ, just as a violet map of a light source will be different from a red map made of the same source. In other words, certain wavelengths are emitted by objects exposed to certain temperatures and certain levels of ionization.

When the number of electrons in an atom matches the number of protons, the atom is neutral. But when the number of electrons is decreased or increased, then the atom is said to be ionized. The material is no longer classified as an atom, but as an ion. And so we have ions of hydrogen or oxygen or any other substance.

Radio astronomy has revealed that the density of ionized hydrogen increases gradually between the solar system and the center of the galaxy. The maximum is reached about 14,000 light-years from the sun, and about 12,000 light-years from the galactic center. Beyond it there is an abrupt dropoff to the center of the galaxy.

Far beyond the ring of ionized gases, and perhaps at the center of the galaxy, radio telescopes detect an extensive source of radio noise, as much as a degree wide. The region appears to be the center of the galaxy. From the observations so far available, it seems that the galactic center is a region where stars are densely packed together: some 5 million apparently within a diameter of only 100 to 200 light-years.

The vast clouds of hydrogen toward the center of the galaxy are not stationary. Rather they are moving outward along the plane of the galaxy at very high speeds. Also, the gas shares in the general rotation of the galaxy. Some ten to twelve thousand light-years from the galactic center the gas slows down. And it changes from neutral hydrogen gas to ionized hydrogen. Apparently, stars condense out of the gases during the interval of some 10 million years required for the gas to move through the region.

If gas is flowing constantly out and away from the galactic center, then there must be some mechanism by which the gases are replenished—astronomers have estimated that all the existing gases would be exhausted in less than 30 million years. Unless the gases are replenished, the galaxy would have to be exploding. Such an idea is difficult to accept.

There are many astronomers who believe that vast amounts of gases flow into the galactic core from the galactic halo, the spherical region inside of which the main part of the galaxy may be contained. It has also been suggested that the material that flows away from the galactic center and along the plane, is replenished by an inflow from intergalactic space. Extremely sensitive radio telescopes may provide a reliable answer to the question concerning the origin of the material that appears to replace the gases that flow at high velocities away from the galactic center. At this time, such identification is not possible.

Structure of the Galaxy (Radio)

Great strides have been made optically in understanding our galaxy. Herschel's star gauging gave boundaries to the "universe"; Shapley's study of globular clusters enabled conceptions of shape and size; and the work of numerous other astronomers added bit by bit to our present understanding of the galaxy in which we live.

But all the conclusions made about the galaxy were determined from limited information. The illustration on page 75 shows how limited was and is our view of the galaxy through the vista afforded by optical telescopes. Only a small volume of the galaxy could be explored.

When you gaze into the nighttime sky on a clear, dark summer night you can see the band of the Milky Way arching across the sky. It is a hazy, cloudlike belt arching through Scorpius, Sagittarius, Aquila, Cygnus, and Cepheus.

Until Galileo was able to discern individual stars by means of his telescope, people believed that the formation was made of weather clouds. Historically, the cloudlike belt of stars had been called *galaxias kyklos,* or "milky circle," by the Greeks. And the Romans called it *via lactea,* which translates literally to "Milky Way."

The broad belt stretches across the sky, making an angle of 62 degrees with the celestial equator. To understand the meaning of these terms, think of the sky as a sphere. Forget that stars and nebulas are at various distances and think of every sky object as being at the same distance from you. If the equator of the earth is extended out to the sky, the "line" running all around the sky is the celestial equator. It cuts the sky in two sections—north and south—just as the terrestrial equator divides the earth into a northern and a southern hemisphere.

When you observe the Milky Way, it cuts across the celestial equator at a 62-degree angle. The equator of the galaxy runs through just about the middle of the Milky Way itself, so we say the equator of the galaxy (the galactic equator) is tilted 62 degrees to the plane of the celestial equator. You can see how the two are related in the drawing on page 85.

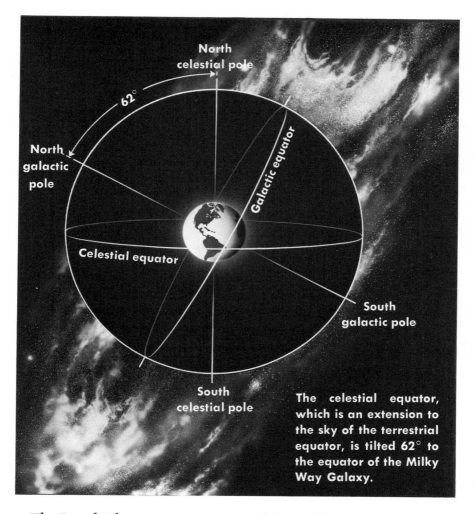

North
celestial pole

62°

North
galactic
pole

Galactic equator

Celestial equator

South
galactic pole

South
celestial pole

The celestial equator,
which is an extension to
the sky of the terrestrial
equator, is tilted 62° to
the equator of the Milky
Way Galaxy.

The Lund Observatory painting of the Milky Way on page 76 shows clearly that most of the stars of our galaxy are concentrated along the plane of the galaxy. Only a few stars are scattered at distances north and south of the plane.

Later on, when radio telescopes were developed to a level where they were quite sensitive, astronomers swung their instruments around the sky. They picked up radio waves instead of light waves. The radio waves were charted and the drawing shown

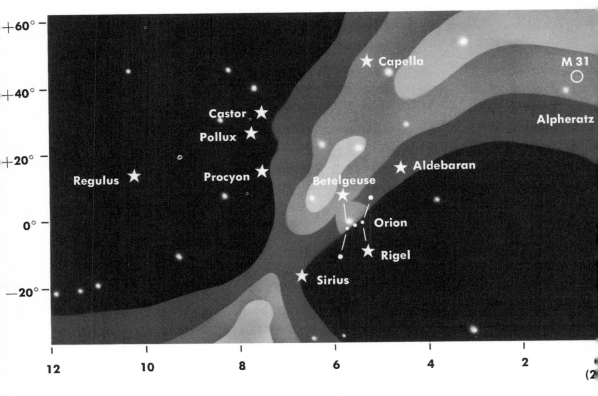

A radio survey of the galaxy made at a wavelength of 120 centimeters at Ohio State University. Notice that greatest intensity is toward the galactic center, and

here resulted. This is the way the sky along the Milky Way would appear if our eyes were sensitive to radio waves rather than light waves. The bright areas show regions from which strong radio energy is received.

The map is a flat projection of a large part of the sphere of the sky. If the left and right ends were joined together and your head were in the middle of the loop, the representation of the sky would be more accurate. You would have to turn your head about to see all of the formation, just as you do when looking at the actual sky.

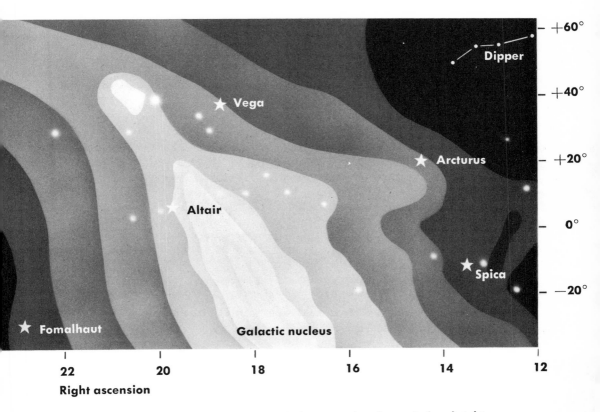

that contours follow generally the plane of the optical galaxy. A few bright objects are plotted to make orientation possible.

This radio view shows the structure of our galaxy, much as an X-ray view of the body shows the skeleton or framework of the body.

Astronomers continued to survey the galaxy with radio telescopes. The "picture" they obtained implied that ours is a spiral galaxy. The study was stimulated by the discovery that our galaxy is spinning in space like a huge wheel. Furthermore, detailed study of other galaxies beyond our own, especially the Andromeda Galaxy, prompted many astronomers to make comparisons between that galaxy and our own.

We are not able to see our galaxy in its entirety, for we are inside of it. But we can see entire galaxies outside our own. After observing the Andromeda Galaxy, astronomers reasoned that since that galaxy is spinning and since it appears to be composed of great "arms" of stars, why should not our spinning galaxy have a similar composition?

The Andromeda Galaxy and other similar galaxies appear to be composed of great lanes or rivers of stars, mostly young, blue stars surrounded by vast areas of ionized gases. Also, the arms appear to contain vast clouds of dust along the edges. Astronomers suspected that ours was a spiral galaxy, and so they looked for formations in our galaxy that were similar to formations observed in other spiral galaxies.

By observing galaxies beyond our own, such as the Andromeda Galaxy shown here, we are able to learn about the structure of our own galaxy.

Great Galaxy in Andromeda

For a long time astronomers knew that there were many blue, hot stars in our galaxy. And each one of them was surrounded by a tremendous cloud of bright hydrogen gas. But the location of the stars in space had not been determined. In the early 1950's astronomers carefully studied the light of these stars and were able to figure out how far away they were. Not only were the stars located, but the distances to clouds of dust and clouds of ionized hydrogen were also computed. When the positions of these formations were plotted on a map of the galaxy, a pattern began to emerge.

Near the sun there were two bands of hydrogen clouds separated by a bank of darkness. When the regions were compared with photographs of the spiral arms in the Andromeda Galaxy, the likeness of the two was apparent. The formations must be spiral arms in our own galaxy. Each section was some 10,000 light-years long, and about 7,000 light-years apart. Our own star, the sun, was at the inner edge of the band that lay closer to the center of the galaxy.

The section of the galaxy in which the sun is located also contains the bright gases of the Orion region, and so it is called the Orion arm. The region beyond contains the bright objects of the Perseus region, and so is called the Perseus arm. Additional studies revealed a third region that is some 4,500 light-years from us toward the center of the galaxy. The bright objects of Sagittarius are located there, and so this third region is called the Sagittarius arm.

These observations made optically were later confirmed by radio investigations. Also the radio telescope revealed an arm far beyond that of Perseus, as well as at least one additional arm located between us and the galactic center.

At the center of our galaxy, toward Sagittarius, there appears to be a brilliant area having a diameter in the order of 20,000 light-years. The region appears to be made primarily of hydrogen gas that is in a state of great turmoil. The first spiral arm of the galaxy lies some 15,000 light-years from the central region. There appears to be a second arm at a distance of some 21,000 light-years; and the Orion arm, in which the sun is, appears to be some 27,000 light-years from the central core. Very likely a nebulous arm exists about 35,000 light-years from the center and the outermost arm is 40,000 light-years or so from the nucleus.

The spiral arms in the vicinity of the sun are becoming more extensively defined all the while. Information about them is incorporated in the drawing below.

Since radio waves can penetrate clouds of dust through which light cannot pass, the radio telescope reveals vast clouds of hydrogen gas at various locations in the galaxy. These are shown in the drawing on page 78.

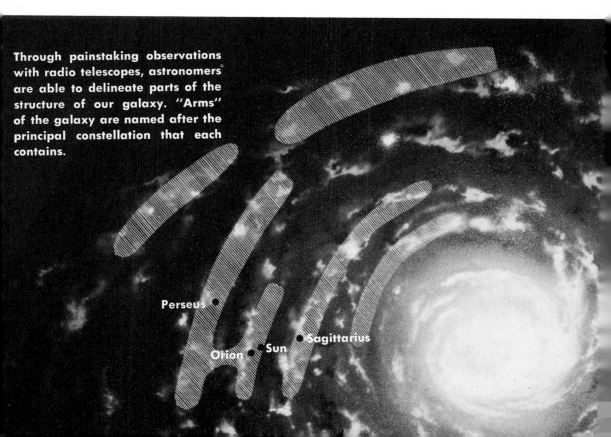

Through painstaking observations with radio telescopes, astronomers are able to delineate parts of the structure of our galaxy. "Arms" of the galaxy are named after the principal constellation that each contains.

Perseus

Orion   Sun   Sagittarius

The entire galaxy has never been observed by earthbound men. But optical and radio observations all indicate that ours is a spiral galaxy. If seen full view it might appear somewhat like Messier 101, a spiral that is in the direction of Ursa Major; edge-on it might appear quite like NGC 891, a galaxy that appears in the direction of the constellation Andromeda. Ours appears to be a spiral galaxy spinning at such a rate that in the location of the sun a rotation is completed in about 250 million years, and the spiral arms are trailing behind. For decades astronomers have been fascinated by the problem of explaining how and why the galaxy

Judging by our present knowledge, we should expect that our galaxy would appear somewhat like Messier 101 (NGC 5457) shown here, if we could view it from above.

If we were able to get out into deep space and look back at our galaxy, it would probably appear much like NGC 891 shown here.

should be a spiral. Many astronomers feel that galactic magnetic fields, small though they may be, play a large part in the story of galactic formation and change.

The galaxy has probably made some fifty turns during its lifetime of 10 billion years. This is longer than the lifetime of the hot young stars that outline the arms. We do not know how the spiral structure is maintained. Perhaps new spiral arms may be continually forming, for otherwise the old arms would have wrapped tightly about one central nucleus.

By means of optical telescopes the magnetic field has been

detected indirectly. If a magnetic field is present between a star and the observer, the effect will be to polarize the starlight. Such polarization can be detected at the telescope in much the same way that it can be detected with Polaroid sunglasses. If you turn the lens of one sunglass at an angle to another, the light is diminished. Extremely delicate and sensitive radio telescopes can also detect polarization of energy from space. All observations indicate that there is a general galactic magnetic field having a strength a few millionths that of the earth's magnetic field near the poles. Even though the field is weak, it may play a part in keeping the spiral arms relatively intact despite their rotation around the galactic nucleus.

Rotation Produces Flattening

Rotation is a condition that is found throughout the universe. Protons in the nuclei of atoms spin, so also do the electrons that revolve around the protons. All the planets rotate, as do all the stars and nebulous formations observed in the galaxy. If a body spins rapidly, it flattens. This is seen in the flattening of the earth itself, and even more so in the flattening of the major planets such as Jupiter and Saturn, both of which spin more rapidly than does the earth. When spiral galaxies outside our own are observed, we note that they are flattened, no doubt because of rapid rotation.

We find it easy to accept that each of the planets is moving around the sun, in response to the sun's gravitational attraction. In a similar fashion we can think of the stars along the galactic plane moving around the center of the galaxy in response to its gravitational attraction.

Mercury, which is the planet closest to the sun, moves most rapidly. As distance from the sun increases, the rate of revolution of the planets decreases. So it is with the stars in the galaxy. The closer the stars are to the nucleus, the faster they move.

Doppler shifts of radio waves reveal motions of interstellar hydrogen. Similarly, motions of stars, especially those near the sun, can be determined by optical observations of starlight. The motions of the stars near the sun might be represented as shown just below. The longer lines of the stars nearer the galactic

Stars close to the nucleus of the galaxy move faster than those farther away. Stars that show a blue shift are approaching (or we are approaching them). Stars that show a red shift are receding (or we are moving away from them).

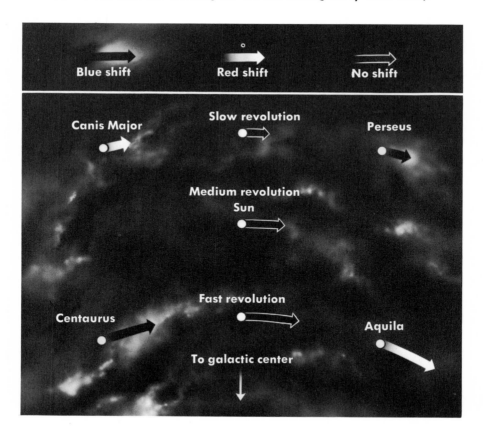

nucleus indicate motion more rapid than those at the distance of the sun, and the shorter lines indicate less rapid motion. But the arrows are represented as the motions would appear from the sun, which is also moving. If the motion of the sun were subtracted from all the observations, then we should be able to represent the actual motions of the stars. Then stars in the direction of Canis Major should show a red shift because we are moving away from them, and stars in the direction of Aquila should also show a red shift because they are moving away from us. Stars in Perseus should show a blue shift because we are catching up to them, and those in the direction of Centaurus should show a blue shift because they are moving toward us. Observations of all these stars bear out predictions—red shifts and blue shifts occur where they should and in the predicted amounts. The conclusion is that at our location the stars are moving toward the Cygnus-Hercules region at a velocity of some 150 miles per second. The velocity is such that a revolution around the center of the galaxy is completed in 230 to 250 million years.

While the sun goes around the center of the galaxy, it also moves above and below the plane of the galaxy.

Right now the sun is about 12 to 15 parsecs north of the galactic plane and it is moving northward at 4 miles a second. The motion is produced mainly by the gravitational attraction of the gases and dust in the galactic plane. The sun will continue to move northward until it is 100 parsecs above the plane of the galaxy; then it will slow down and reverse direction, moving southward, once again pulled by the gravitational attraction of stars and dust that were left behind. The sun will accelerate to a maximum speed of 4 miles a second. It will move 100 parsecs south of the plane, and then reverse once more. And so the sun follows a wavy course as it moves around the center of the galaxy. Eighty million years are needed for one oscillation to be completed.

Orbit of sun

H.K.W.

Stars move above and below the plane of the galaxy as they move around the center. Generally the older stars move greater distances from the plane. (Distances are exaggerated in the drawing.)

Stanley Wyatt, an astronomer at the University of Illinois, has said, "The motion of the sun is somewhat like a horse on a merry-go-round. The main motion of the horse is around the center of the merry-go-round, but at the same time the horse is moving up and down. Three oscillations are completed while the merry-go-round spins around once."

The sun is not peculiar in having this kind of motion. The

motions of some stars, the older ones, are much more extreme. Indeed they may reach 500 light-years above and below the plane, probably because they originated from material that was at that distance. Other stars have very little oscillation. These would generally be the young stars—stars that were formed from material close to or right in the galactic plane.

Motion and change appear to be conditions that prevail throughout the universe. No matter what bodies we study—atoms, the moon, planets, the stars, galaxies, even groups of galaxies— they all are in motion. Similarly, every single formation, no matter how large or small, appears to have an evolutionary history. Certainly this is true of the galaxy, as we shall see in the next chapter.

5

THE EVOLVING GALAXY

IN THE 1920's Edwin P. Hubble, an American astronomer, showed without question that our galaxy was not the entire universe; there was much more to the universe than men had suspected. Our galaxy turned out to be only one of a vast number of galaxies which comprise the universe. The single object that Hubble studied first in detail was the great galaxy in Andromeda (Messier 31). Before Hubble's observations, astronomers believed that the object which bore the number 31 in the list compiled by Messier, the French astronomer, was a formation of relatively nearby gases, some of which were brightly illuminated.

Hubble's initial studies led to years of observing other galaxies and classifying them according to their appearance. Some of the galaxies were spirals of one kind or another; some were irregular with no particular pattern; some were spherical and uniform.

The Milky Way Galaxy appears to be a spiral, perhaps very much like the one shown on page 91. It is classified as an Sb type in the classification which was devised by Hubble and which is often called the "tuning-fork classification," because the dia-

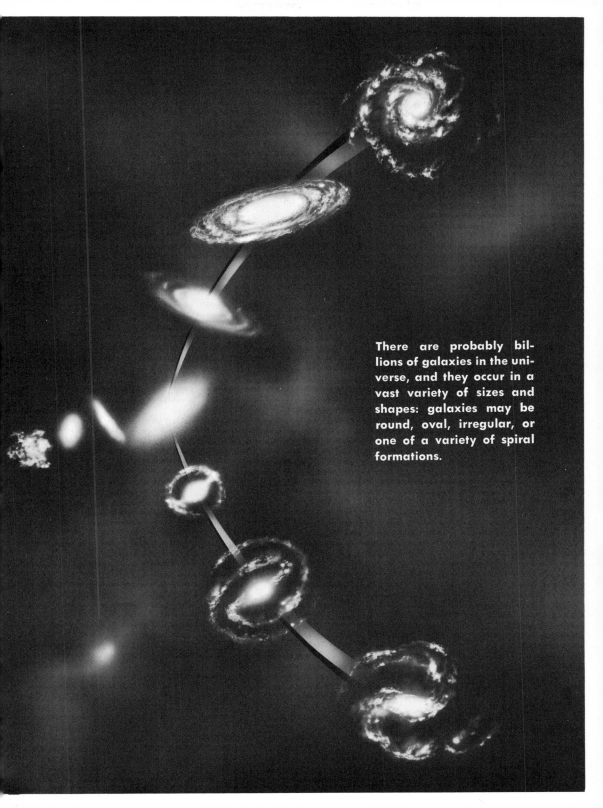

There are probably billions of galaxies in the universe, and they occur in a vast variety of sizes and shapes: galaxies may be round, oval, irregular, or one of a variety of spiral formations.

gram has the shape of a fork-handle and tines. In this system S stands for spiral, and the *b* represents a stage in development between a tight spiral and a loose one.

The shape of a spiral galaxy suggests rapid spinning motion. But there is no way of observing this motion when the galaxy is seen in full view. However, when a galaxy is viewed edge-on, Doppler shifts of the light from the edges of the formation can be observed, thus revealing that one edge is moving toward us while the other edge is moving away. When such observations were possible, one was looking at the galaxy edge-on, and since the view was edge-on, he could not see whether or not the galaxy was a spiral. Therefore, astronomers could not say whether the arms of a galaxy were trailing or whether they were leading, as though the formation were unwinding.

From considerations other than observation, it seems that the arms of spiral galaxies must trail. The inner parts of galaxies rotate more rapidly than do the outer regions. Therefore the outer regions must trail behind the inner regions. But, if this is so, then the stars in any spiral arm should form into a ring of stars around the nucleus after only two or three turns.

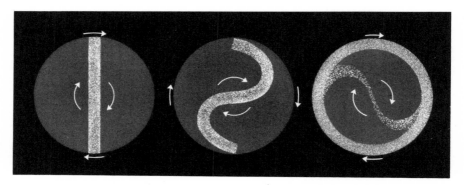

The dynamics of rotation are such that stars in a galaxy should form into a ring after a turn or two.

Many different observations lead to the conclusion that our galaxy is 10 billion years old, and it has made fifty turns. Therefore, there must be some force at work which prevents the arms from evolving into circular formations, or new arms must continually form.

Another puzzle about the spiral arms perplexes astronomers. Many of the stars in the spiral arms are hot, blue-white stars that produce energy at stupendous rates; so rapidly that they cannot last more than a few million years. The stars should be burned out unless new stars are being created as old stars go out of existence.

Astronomers note that not only are the spiral arms rich in blue, young stars, but the arms also contain large quantities of cosmic dust and gases. It is believed that these gases provide the raw materials out of which new stars are created. But such an explanation cannot be accepted unless one is able to suggest a manner in which the gases, the raw material of stars, can be replenished. Astronomers have estimated that the gas available in a spiral arm would be consumed in less than a billion years. If the galaxy is 10 billion years old, and if stars are being created today, as seems to be the case, then the gases must be replenished in some manner. It is probable that some objects, like novas and planetary nebulas, are injecting gas into the interstellar medium. Perhaps the gas flows out to the arms from the denser nucleus of the galaxy, as suggested earlier. Or perhaps the rate of star formation slows down as age increases, thus extending the lifetime of the gases. Perhaps so, but whatever the explanation, one is pressed to explain how it is that the gases persist in the arms rather than diffusing into the space between the arms.

Part of the answer may have been found in 1949 when investigators determined that the galaxy possesses a magnetic field.

In 1957 another answer to the problem of the replenishment of material in the spiral arms of the galaxy was found. A flow of gas toward the sun and from the center of the galaxy was indicated. Every year the total amount of the gases is about equal to the mass of the sun. Some astronomers believe that the gases flow along magnetic lines of force in the spiral arms. Also, they believe that the gases are sufficient to explain the origin of the material from which new stars are formed. They believe that there is enough material to allow for some leakage into space from the spiral arms.

The location of the axis of the galactic magnetic field is not known certainly. However, it has been suggested that the magnetic field originally might have been as shown on page 103. In the core of the galaxy ionized atoms, which carry an electric charge, would have been closely held by the magnetic field. As the galaxy rotated, the gases would have been thrown outward and the magnetic lines of force would have been elongated as shown. Forever after, material ejected out of the core of the galaxy would tend to follow these same lines, thus reenforcing the spiral arms.

The illustration on page 99 of Hubble's tuning-fork diagram is an attempt to arrange the different types of galaxies according to their shape and appearance. It is not meant to imply an evolution from left to right, or right to left, for that matter.

Galaxies have not been observed for a long enough period for anyone to determine whether a certain form of galaxy evolves into another, or vice versa. When we observe different kinds of galaxies—spirals, ellipticals, sphericals—we probably are not observing stages in evolution. We are more likely observing entirely different "species" of galaxies that are not related one to another in terms of age or progression.

It is quite normal for one to wonder how different "species" of galaxies might have developed.

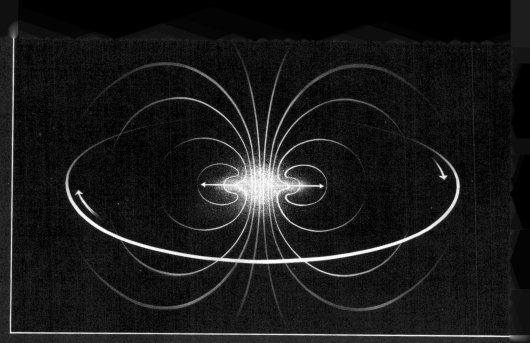

Originally the magnetic field of a galaxy may be as above. Gases are bound tightly to the magnetic lines of force.

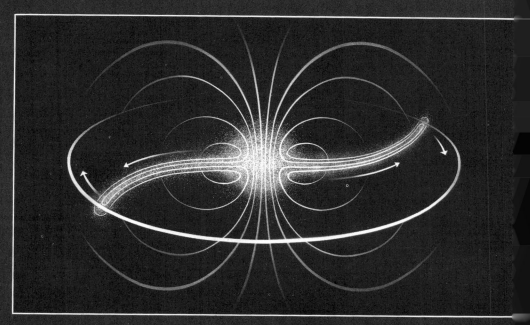

As gas in the nucleus is thrown outward, lines of magnetic force are pulled along. Additional material would follow these lines and form the arms.

Let us suppose that the universe began with a tremendous explosion some 10 billion years ago. As soon as the explosion occurred, space was filled with material, and the material was evenly distributed. However, the situation changed rapidly, for small islands where the materals were more densely arranged developed rapidly. These dense islands were galaxies in the process of formation. There would be no reason why the masses of all these denser islands should be identical. On the contrary, one would expect that masses would vary a great deal. Also, one would expect that the density throughout an island would not be uniform. Some areas would be more dense than others, and a general motion of the mass would be introduced.

An island of gaseous material would be expected to contract. As the materials packed more tightly, they would spin more rapidly. This speed-up in rotation can be experienced while spinning on ice skates or on a piano stool. If you extend your arms, you spin more slowly. Hug yourself, and you spin more rapidly.

Some astronomers believe that if a protogalaxy, a galaxy in the process of formation, spun too rapidly it might break up or it might throw large masses of material into space. If a protogalaxy were rotating slowly, it could decrease in size, pack closer together, without breaking apart. The material could pack together tightly enough for stars to form. It is believed that the spherical and elliptical galaxies might have been formed in some such manner.

If a mass of material were spinning more rapidly, it could not pack together as tightly. Also large amounts of material would be separated from the central mass and thrown into space. This would mean that a slowly moving galaxy could be much more massive than one that rotates rapidly. This seems to be the case, although observations of galactic motion are not as numerous, nor as reliable, as astronomers would like to have them.

The Milky Way Galaxy appears to be a spiral. Gases appear to move out into the spiral arms from the central region. Perhaps these gases are recirculating as mentioned above. Perhaps they originate in the galactic halo, or they may come from the vastness of intergalactic space.

Because the mass of our galaxy is so much less than the mass of an elliptical, it seems unlikely that eventually the galaxy would become an elliptical or spheroidal formation. But the change may not be one of evolution. Who knows, maybe this is the way a galaxy matures normally; maybe a spiral formation is merely a stage in normal growth and development.

How Old and How Long?

To review, let's start at the beginning and see if we can reconstruct the processes and changes that may have occurred in our galaxy.

Radioactive dating of basic rocks in the crust of the earth, studies of the layering of sedimentary formations, and theories of the time required for substances to combine into organized systems indicate that the earth is about 5 billion years old. If we accept that all the planets and their satellites had a similar origin, then it is reasonable to say that our solar system is on the order of 5 billion years old. Our estimate of the age of the stellar system is based on much flimsier knowledge. However, it seems reasonable to say that the galaxy has been in existence something like 10 billion years, perhaps considerably longer.

There was probably a time when our galaxy was nothing more than a great mass of hydrogen gas. The volume and shape of the mass, if it had any shape at all, was somewhat larger than the volume of our present galaxy, including the entire halo. And very likely there was a time when the gases formed into a rough spherical agglomeration.

Every single bit of matter exerts a gravitational attraction on every other particle. And so each individual atom that composed the primeval gas from which the galaxy evolved pulled on the other atoms. Those close by were affected most strongly, causing groups of the atoms to cluster together. In the nature of things, these clusters would have collected additional atoms, and so the mass of the cluster would grow steadily. There would have been constant motion—the gases swirling about and mixing together, individual atoms in disorganized, unpredictable flight.

After scores of millenniums had passed, a degree of order would have become established. The random motions would have assumed a degree of predictability. The entire mass of material would have contracted to a smaller size, pulled in by the gravitational attraction of collections of clusters. Trajectory curves would have been introduced. And the entire mass would have assumed some uniformity of motion—a slow rotation would have developed. The rate of rotation would become greater as millions of years went by because the volume would continue to get smaller as the gases were packed together more tightly. But at this early stage, the motion was slow. Density of the material grew steadily.

All through these stages there was constant motion of individual atoms, and there was constant motion of clusters of atoms. Currents built up and then collapsed, simply because of inability of the mass to hold together. After some time, however, the density of the clusters became greater. When currents developed, they could be sustained. The density of the clusters was sufficient for the motion to be sustained. More and more material was attracted to the individual clusters. Where originally the entire galaxy had been nothing more than disassociated gases, it had now become considerably more organized.

The clusters grew as more and more material was attracted to them. Gravitational attraction packed the matter together tightly, and so increased temperature. When the temperature reached some 10 million degrees, nuclear fusion reactions were initiated. The mass had become a star. Stars formed at this stage are the very old stars of our galaxy. The most noteworthy are those that are found in the globular clusters that occupy the galactic halo.

These early stars and clusters of stars, immersed though they were in the nebulous gases of the new galaxy, were unaffected by those gases. But the mass of the total material exerted a strong gravitational effect on the newly formed stars and star clusters, determining the orbits they were to follow. Since the stars formed at a time when the speed of rotation of the galaxy was slow, the speed of these old stars in their journey around the galactic center is slow, considerably less than that of stars formed more recently.

Some of the old stars were formed from gas and dust close to the galactic plane; others were formed from material at various distances from the plane. Old stars composed of material far from the galactic plane—deep in the galactic halo—travel in orbits that rise high above the galactic plane, passing up and down through it at intervals of some hundred million years (see diagram on page 96).

The very old stars used up only a small part of the hydrogen of the galaxy. The rest of it continued to contract and increase in density. The composition of the gases of the protogalaxy was gradually changed as new elements produced in the original stars were added. Stars are vast nuclear reactors in which the nuclei of lighter elements are fused to produce nuclei of heavier elements. For example, four hydrogen nuclei combine to produce a single helium nucleus. Other combinations produce lithium, beryllium, boron, fluorine, oxygen. Many of these and other elements made in the primary stars were ejected out of the stars, and mixed with the original hydrogen.

Hydrogen still comprised well over 99 percent of the total, but

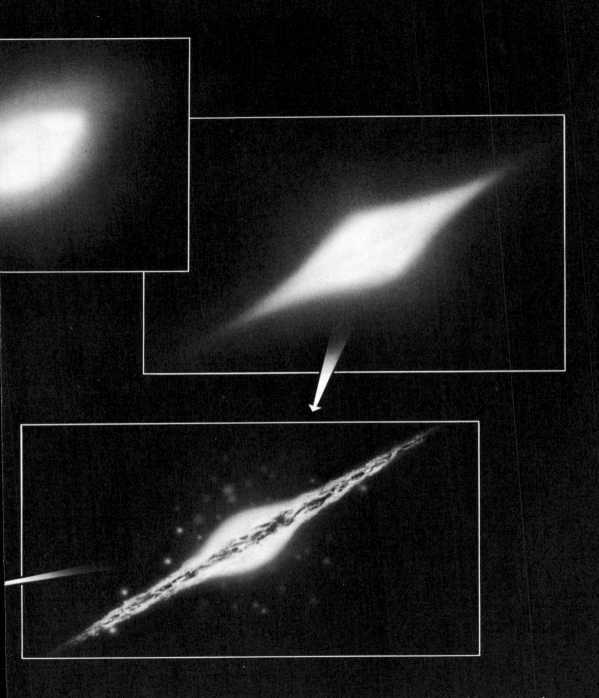

During some 10 to 15 billion years a great mass of gases (maybe nothing more than hydrogen nuclei) may have gradually evolved into the galaxy as it is now—a galaxy containing upward of 100 billion stars, having a diameter of 100 light-years, and, as far as we are concerned, rightfully called Galaxy Number One.

several other and heavier elements were also present. The gases continued to contract. As they did, the speed of rotation built up steadily, and the spherical mass became elongated and flattened to some degree. Now another generation of stars was formed. But they were different from the original ones. These stars were built from the original hydrogen as well as the new elements contributed by the primary stars. Also, they moved in tighter orbits around the galactic nucleus, for they were formed from materials that were encased within a halo that had shrunk from the original size. These newer stars revolved in flatter orbits than the older, first-generation, stars for they formed when the gases of the galaxy had assumed a flatter and less round shape, and they rotated more slowly than does the sun. This is because the rotation of the gaseous formation from which the stars were formed was slow.

Billions of years went by, and the great spherical mass of gases became steadily flatter. As the formation flattened, density increased, and additional generations of stars were created. These younger stars were considerably richer than the primeval stars in the elements beyond hydrogen and helium.

The gases rotated more rapidly as they contracted. But a time was reached when they no longer contracted. At this stage additional generations of stars were created, the sun among them. These later stars were formed from material in the disk of the galaxy, and so they remain there. They move very little vertically, but move rapidly around the galactic nucleus, since they were formed from gases that were in rapid rotation.

But stars formed along with the sun did not mark the end of stellar creation, for stars are being created right now. However, the rate of formation has decreased a great deal, simply because there is not as much raw material as there used to be.

As far as astronomers can determine, stars are not being formed in the halo of the galaxy. You would expect them to originate where the gases are most dense. This would mean the galactic disk. Stellar formation occurs almost exclusively in the spiral arms of the galaxy, and the composition of these stars is rich in the heavier elements. The hydrogen in these young stars is for the most part hydrogen that was in the original mass, while the heavier elements are contributed by the older stars, the elements having been built by nuclear fusion reactions within them.

One quite naturally wonders how long this star-making process can continue, or is it something that goes on forever? As mentioned earlier, star making can continue only as long as raw material is available. At the present time just about 98 percent of the material in the galaxy is contained in stars. Only about 2 percent is in the form of dust and gases, mostly contained in the spiral arms of the galactic disk. This gas will be augmented by gases lost into space from existing stars. For billions of years stars will continue to be created from these gases. Eventually, however, the creation of a star within our galaxy will be a rare event, for the only raw material available will be the matter that is lost to space from other, and older, stars.

Therefore, the percentage of new and bright stars in our galaxy will drop steadily. The only kinds of stars left will be dim, red stars. There will be little, if any, gas remaining in the galaxy and our spiral structure will have deteriorated into a tight sphere or ellipsoid surrounded by a dull red halo, and cut through by a brighter red disk. For untold millenniums red will be the dominant color in our galaxy. Finally, even that color will fade, and vibrant, dynamic stars in bright blues, greens, and brilliant hot white will have become dim, dull, dark masses revolving relentlessly around the central mass of the inert galaxy.

Finding Stellar Magnitudes

For Those Who Understand Logarithms

For those of you who are interested in the mathematics involved in the computation we include here the steps that are followed in finding stellar magnitudes.

When the brightness of a star is known, and also its distance, the absolute magnitude can be found by using this equation:

$M = m + 5 - 5 \log d$

M = absolute magnitude

m = apparent magnitude

d = distance in parsecs

To see how we get M, let's first see how we get apparent magnitude. Astronomers use a geometric or log (logarithmic) scale for referring to magnitudes. To obtain apparent magnitude, the brightness of the star is measured with a light meter. The magnitude value is then obtained as follows:

$$m = -2.5 \log b$$

The brightness of the star is b. The —2.5 comes from the agreed relationship between magnitudes—that is, a first-magnitude star is 2.5 times brighter than a second-magnitude star.

Let's see how this works for a typical star. Suppose the observed brightness of the star figures out to have a value of 4.4, the apparent magnitude of the star would be:

$$m = -2.5 \log 4.4$$
$$= -2.5 \times 0.64 \ (0.64 \text{ is the log of } 4.4)$$
$$= -1.6$$

Once we have obtained the apparent magnitude of a star, then we can use that information in the equation for absolute magnitude:

$$M = m + 5 - 5 \log d$$

The absolute magnitude of a star is the brightness the star would have at a distance of 10 parsecs (A parsec is the distance an object would be if it had a *par*allax of one *sec*ond, or 3.26 light-years.) Values for absolute magnitude are assigned the same way as those for apparent magnitude. However, b in the equation for apparent brightness is replaced by B, brightness at 10 parsecs:

$$M = -2.5 \log B$$

Knowing the brightness by observation, and knowing the apparent magnitude, we can find B by using this equation:

$$B = b \times \left(\frac{d}{10}\right)^2$$

In other words, B is related to b as the square of the distance to the star. And this is related to 10 parsecs squared. We square the distance because light falls off as the square of the distance.

Because

$$B = b\left(\frac{d}{10}\right)^2$$

we can use this value for B in the equation for absolute magnitude:

$$M = -2.5 \log B$$

$$M = -2.5 \log \left[b\left(\frac{d}{10}\right)^2\right]$$

Now we must find the log of $b\left(\frac{d}{10}\right)^2$.

In logs when we square a number, we give it a log 2. Therefore, $\left(\frac{d}{10}\right)^2$ becomes $2 \times (\log d - \log 10)$.

You recall that when you divide logs, you subtract the numbers. Now we have

$$M = -2.5 \log [b + 2 \times (\log d - \log 10)]$$
$$M = -2.5 \log b$$
$$-2.5 \times \quad 2 \log \ d = -5 \ \log d$$
$$-2.5 \times -2 \log 10 = \quad 5 \quad \log 10 \ (\log 10 \text{ is } 1,$$
$$\text{so we get simply } 5)$$

Put in better form:

$$M = -2.5 \log b - 5 \log d + 5$$

We already know that $-2.5 \log b$ equals m, therefore:

$$M = m + 5 - 5 \log d$$

Let's see how the equation works with a star, such as Sirius. It has an apparent magnitude (m) of -1.42 and its distance is

8.7 light-years. We change light-years to parsecs by dividing 8.7 by 3.26 = 2.67 parsecs.

$$M = m + 5 - 5 \log d$$
$$= -1.42 + 5 - 5 \log 2.67$$
$$\log 2.67 = 0.4265$$
$$= -1.42 + 5 - 5 \times 0.4265$$
$$= -1.42 + 5 - 2.1325$$
$$= 1.4475, \text{ the absolute magnitude of Sirius}$$

Finding Stellar Distance from Magnitudes

To find the distance to a star when its magnitudes are known, we change the equation for absolute magnitude:

$$M = m + 5 - 5 \log d$$

to

$$5 \log d = m - M + 5$$

$$\log d = \frac{m - M + 5}{5}$$

$$d = \text{antilog} \frac{(m - M + 5)}{5}$$

An antilog is the number which a log drawn to base 10 would produce; the antilog of 2 is 100, of 3 is 1,000, of 4 is 10,000, and so on. Let's substitute in this equation the values for a hypothetical star having an apparent magnitude of 10 and an absolute magnitude of 0.

$$d = \text{antilog} \frac{(m - M + 5)}{5}$$

$$= \text{antilog} \frac{(10 - 0 + 5)}{5}$$

$$= \text{antilog} \frac{(15)}{5}$$

$$= \text{antilog of } 3$$

$$d = 1{,}000 \text{ parsecs, or}$$
$$3{,}260 \text{ light-years}$$

Galactic Data

DIAMETER	100,000 light-years
THICKNESS (CENTER)	15,000 light-years
THICKNESS (NEAR SUN)	1,300 light-years
DIAMETER OF GLOBULAR CLUSTER SYSTEM	160,000 light-years
GALACTIC EQUATOR	inclined 62° to celestial equator. Crosses S to N in Aquila, and N to S a bit east of Orion
GALACTIC NORTH POLE	RA 12h40m, Decl. +28° (the location of Coma Berenices)
GALACTIC SOUTH POLE	RA 0^n 40m, Decl. −28° (the location of Sculptor)
GALACTIC LONGITUDE	measured eastward from where the galactic plane crosses the equator RA 18^h40^m, Decl. 0°
GALACTIC LATITUDE	degrees north or south of the galactic equator
DIRECTION OF REVOLUTION (OF SUN AREA)	toward galactic longitude 90°
PERIOD OF REVOLUTION (OF SUN AREA)	220 million years
VELOCITY OF MOTION (OF SUN AREA)	150 miles a second

VELOCITY OF MOTION ....

Distance from Center kpsc	Velocity (km/sec)
1	150
2	180
4	210
6	225
8.2	215

RA = Right ascension
Decl. = Declination
Parsec = 3.26 light-years
Kpsc (kiloparsec) = 1,000 parsecs
Kilometer = miles × 0.621

DEGREE OF FLATTENING 1/6
DIRECTION OF CENTER .... 0° (Sagittarius region)
DISTANCE OF SUN FROM CENTER .... 25,000 to 35,000 light-years
DISTANCE OF SUN FROM
    GALACTIC PLANE .... 12 to 15 parsecs (PSC) north

VELOCITY OF ESCAPE:	galactic center	450 km/sec
	solar region	290 km/sec
	rim of galaxy	180 km/sec

NUMBER OF ATOMS IN THE GALAXY ...... 10^{68}
NUMBER OF STARS IN THE GALAXY .... 130,000,000,000 (1.3×10^{11}) (?)
MASS OF GALACTIC DISK .... 1.1×10^{11} to 1.3×10^{11} solar
    masses (?)
MASS OF TOTAL GALAXY .... 2×10^{11} solar masses (?)
DENSITY .... 7×10^{-24} g/cm^3
    0.1 solar masses per cubic parsec
ABSOLUTE MAGNITUDE .... —20.5
AGE .... 1.0 to 1.5×10^{10} years

FOR FURTHER READING

Abell, George. *Exploration of the Universe.* New York: Holt, Rinehart and Winston, 1964.

Asimov, Isaac. *The Universe.* New York: Walker and Company, 1966.

Bok, Bart and Priscilla. *The Milky Way.* Cambridge: Harvard University Press, 1957.

Hubble, Edwin. *The Realm of the Nebulae.* New Haven: Yale University Press, 1936.

Page, Thornton (Ed.). *Stars and Galaxies.* Englewood Cliffs, New Jersey: Prentice-Hall, 1962.

Pfeiffer, John. *The Changing Universe.* New York: Random House, 1956.

Pickering, James S. *Windows to Space.* Boston: Little, Brown and Company, 1967.

Shapley, Harlow, *A Sourcebook in Astronomy.* Cambridge: Harvard University Press, 1960.

Struve, Otto. *The Universe.* Cambridge: Massachusetts Institute of Technology Press, 1962.

Wyatt, Stanley. *Principles of Astronomy.* Boston: Allyn and Bacon, 1966.

INDEX